GW00400416

A Steeplejack's View of Life

St. Bartholomew's Church, Rogate

A Steeplejack's View of Life

Peter Harknett

STEEPLEJACK PUBLISHING

Some of the work of steeplejacks

STEEPLEJACK PUBLISHING
10 Barnside Way • Liss • Hampshire • GU33 7LN
steeplejack@harknett.co.uk

First published in Great Britain in 2018

ISBN 978-1-912804-37-5

Printed and bound in Great Britain by
Biddles Books • King's Lynn • Norfolk • PE32 1SF

Contents

Introduction

I have spent the bulk of my working life sitting on a short length of scaffolding board on the end of a rope. Sitting there, well above the ground and with a decent amount of space beneath my feet, admiring the view and occasionally working, gives me plenty of time to think about life in general and some of the country crafts and folks that I met along the way.

Sitting in a bosun's chair on a village church spire, you feel that you could be in almost any century. All you hear is the country noises of tractors droning away in the distance, the birds singing and the monotonous sound of my shingler's axe driving in very modern nails. You look at those nails and you are jerked back into modern life again. You suddenly realise that the droning of a tractor is the sound of a nearby motorway, and the country noises are your block pulleys in need of oil, and your thoughts go back to the job in hand, which in my case is usually reshingling the spire, but as you take the old shingles off you always start thinking about the people who shingled it before.

As you remove the shingles you see evidence of even earlier coverings, you then start wondering about their lives and their problems. Their lives would have been much simpler than ours but at the same time much harder. You know that the shingles would have been made very locally and all split by hand, possibly by the same men who had fixed them, maybe a couple of centuries ago. Things would have been very different, certainly much harder, longer hours for less money. As you are thinking this, the phone rings and one of the men on the ground tells you: "Tea's up!"

This book is not meant to be an autobiography, nor is it in any way meant to be technically correct. The illustrations are just hand-drawn sketches, sometimes with handrails missing for clarity. Some are out of proportion and in some the perspective is completely wrong. They are there to give the lay person some idea as to what I am talking about.

Over the years I have given talks and lectures to many organisations such as museums, universities, churches and cathedrals, also many talks to local history societies and village communities etc. All have been well received, but not always understood. In this book I try to explain more about the craft of steeplejacking for the uninitiated, with plenty of opportunity for the professionals to laugh and criticise. I try to tell the readers the stories that I use in my talks together with a few more, also a little bit of history, hoping to encourage more people to get interested in the conservation of our heritage.

Although I tell several stories about the industrial side of the craft, it is church-repairing steeplejacking that I aim for. Perhaps this book will encourage more professionals from the industrial side to put pen to paper. I have spent the last ten years training and trying to encourage a group of roofers in the craft of church-repairing steeplejacking. All of them have really enjoyed the work and the height and are now very capable of doing the job well and safely.

Chapter One

The Craft

It is generally accepted that the craft of steeplejacking originated during the 16th century, when teams of acrobats travelled around the country giving performances to the local residents. Because of problems with transporting their equipment they used the local amenities, e.g. tall trees, the local maypole (these were often much taller than you would expect) and of course the church tower or spire. They would climb up the inside of the tower or spire and out through the small lookout door situated near the top, fix their ropes and equipment and perform their acts of daring. After the show, the vicar often asked them to repair the spire as they had the access to reach the tiles etc. They soon realised that there was more money in repairing than doing the performance.

Several set up small gangs and started repairing church spires as a way of making a living, learning parts of trades as they went along. People started calling them "steeplejacks of all trades", which very soon got shortened to "steeplejacks".

This was the start of the church-repairing steeplejacks who trade today.

Later, with the coming of the railways and the industrial revolution, with tall buildings, mills, chimney stacks, bridges and viaducts, there was a need for a different type of steeplejack, one more suited to heavy building work and rigging--the industrial steeplejack. A lot of people will argue that the church-repairing steeplejack and the industrial steeplejack are one and the same. But even though they do both types of work, they usually specialise in one or the other.

It was the needs of the Great Western Railway that brought the industrial steeplejack to prominence. The Great Western Railway had many problems. One was to lay a permanent way that did not have steep gradients. It seemed that even with the great weight of the locomotives there was a problem of traction on gradients. This meant that the engineers either had to dig cuttings or tunnel through obstacles. But when they came to valleys, the viaduct was the answer. When at last the railway had crossed the Tamar and arrived in Cornwall there was a need for several viaducts. Cornwall has no clay for bricks and transporting clay from Devon would have been a very slow and expensive exercise. The costs of access for centring to build a series of arches would have caused serious financial problems.

The chief engineer for the Great Western Railway at that time was Isambard Kingdom Brunel. He designed a viaduct that consisted of a series of piers across the valley with a timber railroad spanning the gaps between the piers and therefore the valley. These viaducts were amazing constructions, like timber gantries cantilevered from pier to pier.

Brunel had these viaducts constructed from Baltic pine. It is a very durable timber, but as they got older they needed repairs and Baltic pine became very expensive. So he used Oregon pine, which wasn't as durable – so more frequent repairs were necessary. Brunel realised that the only way to repair viaducts would be by roped access, as there would be a lot of rigging and heavy lifting. He employed several gangs of jolly jack tars, whose naval training with rope work would be invaluable. I believe these men were some of the earliest industrial steeplejacks. I am equally sure that as an island there were similar situations occurring round the country.

Even today, with all the television coverage and the many booklets that have been written about steeplejacks, an awful lot of people have no idea what a steeplejack is or does. A steeplejack is a person who works safely at height without the use of conventional scaffolding, but uses the building to support his rigging.

Modern day buildings often have internal access, so it is only a matter of hauling up and rigging, but on older buildings and structures you have to make your own access up the outside, usually by laddering up. This is probably the most important part of the steeplejack's craft, because without the art of laddering an awful lot of buildings that we work on would have to be scaffolded.

To the uninitiated, watching someone laddering looks somewhat precarious but done correctly, it is perfectly safe. When a steeplejack arrives on site, the first thing he does is to walk around the base of the tower or chimney looking for the best elevation to ladder. He always looks for the tell-tale marks that show where the last steeplejack had fixed his ladders. (If possible, we try to use the same holes as this saves a lot of work cutting new ones.)

The method of laddering varies from gang to gang. We usually like to use the old way, which is to drive a fixing approximately five feet up, stand a ten foot ladder against the structure and tie the ladder with the irons sometimes referred to as 'averages' to hold the ladder approximately a foot away from the wall. Then the steeplejack climbs the ladder and "legs in" (hooks his leg over the top rung). He then reaches up, puts in another fixing and shouts to his mate, who passes him another ladder. This he slots into the first ladder and ties, repeating the process until he reaches the top. Normally we fix just one fixing per ten foot ladder, but if the steeplejack is not satisfied with the fixing he would put in another. Safety is the first priority.

Once the steeplejack reaches the top of a spire and stops admiring the view he can rig his bosun's chair, from which he can rig a platform that is fully boarded and hand-railed. From this he and his mates can safely carry out any work.

The craft of steeplejacks is made up with parts of trades. There used to be a very good system where if you had, say, a three-handed gang, all men of equal experience in jacking, whoever was best at that particular job part would take charge and the others would assist him. There was never an argument about who had the shout, who went down to get the tea on or bring up any tools that had been forgotten.

One of the most important parts of the job is security. Whenever a site is left unattended it is necessary to pull up all ropes out of reach and remove the lower ladders. It is amazing how a steeplejack site always attracts the wrong type of visitor. You always get the local hero – usually from the public house that always seems to be near the church. On a summer evening with a few pints inside him, the hero, who has been bragging about his climbing skills, suddenly wants to prove just how good he is. You also get the guys with the Transit vans looking for a bit of scrap lead. They always seem to want fishing weights. Another thing that the heroes specialise in is leaving evidence of their visit by putting a traffic cone on the weathervane or some ladies' underwear, trying to prove that they can 'pull' as well as climb!

Because, generally speaking, steeplejacks are capable of overcoming any problem of access, they get asked to do many different jobs, including lowering themselves down wells or mineshafts, or removing items of clothing (usually women's underwear) from statues or flagpoles. We have even been asked to rescue animals from cliffs.

Once while driving my van between jobs I was listening to the radio when I heard that there had been a large cliff fall above a small fishing village in Cornwall. It seemed that this had been the site of a serious accident many years before when a rock fall had hit the fishery processing building, killing a man. The fishery was still trading and there was concern for the safety of the workers. When I got back to my yard and office I found that there had been an enquiry about the rock fall that I'd heard about while driving. Thinking that it was an emergency, I drove down to Cornwall that evening. In those days the roads were not as good as they are today and so it was in the small hours when I arrived. Luckily, I had telephoned earlier for digs.

First thing in the morning I went to the cliff where the problem was. I needn't have worried, as the local council had put large wooden sleepers around the fishery and had stopped the staff from entering the premises. After a meeting with the interested parties it was decided that I would range over the whole cliff face to remove any dangerous or loose stones.

The cliff was not very stable and it was quite a problem to get a safe fixing for a bosun's chair, so I drove my van around the back of a hill and up a steep slope to get above the cliff. There were no trees, only small stumpy bushes. So I parked my van sideways to the cliff face and anchored my bosun's chair to it. A couple of days later, my job was well done. I lived on Porthleven crab and mussels for some time; at least their store and warehouse were open again for business.

A church steeplejack needs a good knowledge of blacksmithing to enable him to discuss his needs with the blacksmith. A blacksmith is unlikely to want to climb up to take dimensions or offer advice on the best method, so the steeplejack needs to be able to take a detail of what is required and to sketch this out. He also needs this knowledge to advise the church, and as he gets more experience he will have seen and worked on the many different types of weathervanes and finials, and can estimate to what extent they have weathered. This knowledge will be invaluable to the church or any other client in the future.

There is also a need for a good understanding of rope work, i.e. knots, bends and splicing, together with an understanding of the types of ropes needed for the different jobs. As the use of the old timber batten decks gets less and less, and the use of scaffold tube and fittings for the flying decks, of which we are so proud, becomes more popular, a basic knowledge of scaffolding will become essential.

These days we use much more safety equipment and a lot of it is from mountaineering and potholing. This equipment is so much lighter and so much better in the wet and dirty conditions that we encounter every winter.

Chapter Two

Getting Started

For many years you work for others, try other occupations, do your National Service, gain a lot of experience and hopefully grow up a bit.

My National Service was a complete failure – I was just not cut out to be a soldier. But there were some good times. I experienced rock climbing, abseiling, canoeing and parachuting and learned about the importance of loyalty and cameraderie.

So when I got my release from full-time service I was in a quandary about what to do with the rest of my life. There was a song going around about Nellie the Elephant running away from the circus. I heard it as running away *to* the circus, though, and thought, what's good enough for Nellie is good enough for me. So I joined Bertram Mills Circus, then at their winter quarters, as a rigger.

Working on a circus was not quite what I had expected, but I did the Scottish tour and one Olympia, met some great characters, had a great time, earned a living and learned a lot. After my time working as an elephant's mate I decided to try on my own.

It is not an easy job to get started. The vast majority of the buildings we work on are important historically and a lot are listed. Until you have completed a few contracts successfully nobody is willing to trust you on their building so you have to go 'repping': knocking on doors, trying to convince people that you are genuine and not just looking for a handout.

There are many stories about cold calling. One that comes to mind is a Catholic church in Surrey. I had noticed some problems on the tower as I had driven past on several occasions, but on this morning I decided to stop and chat with the priest. I knocked on his door and to my surprise and relief he opened it with a smile. I explained the problem that I had noticed with his tower. He seemed very interested but his main concern was insurance, so I explained to him that we were

fully insured and any problem at the end of the job would be put right at no extra cost. He wasn't the slightest bit worried about the building; his only concern was the safety of our men. He seemed extremely nervous about our men working on his tower. However, he gave us the job and in due course we turned up with our ladders etc. and started to fix them up the wall.

When the priest looked out of his door, he was horrified and so worried about us that he just could not look and shot back indoors. As the job progressed he got more and more used to watching and got quite relaxed, almost blasé. So when some friends of his turned up, who like him were very nervous, he started to show off. He was looking up at us swinging about on our ropes, saying to his friends: "You get used to watching", "They're quite safe up there", "They know exactly what they're doing", when he tripped over the kerb and broke his leg.

When you start on your own you have to take almost any job that is offered. One of the first jobs we were offered was to paint a large cement silo. It was a very dirty, unpleasant job for very little money. But every job helps to get you known and trusted. So for the next couple of years or so we worked on painting silos, pylons and a lot of uninteresting buildings, but always looking for work on local churches and public buildings. I always kept an eye on the trade and construction papers, as it's good to know what is going on around the world. At that time (early 1960s) I noticed that the Ministry of Works was looking for tenders to remove the bell from St. Stephen's Tower to get it repaired and replaced.

It is well known that when this bell was first put into the tower it cracked and was taken out and back to the foundry. It was eventually brought back to the tower and rehung, where apparently when the clock struck, the bell cracked again. Probably because of expense and the need to get the building completed, it was decided to leave it cracked. I imagine at that time they had not put a roof on the tower, making it so much easier to lift the bell out, but of course in the 60s there was a roof and that's probably why no one tendered for the job. I think my application was treated as a joke.

Another large contract that we applied for was to straighten the Leaning Tower of Pisa. I had read in the newspaper that it was in imminent danger of falling. So I spent the whole of the Passover holiday working on drawings of my ideas. They didn't want to straighten the tower, as there wouldn't be much interest in the Straight Tower of Pisa. They wanted to hold the tower while they strengthened it. They had already been in touch with several large companies with different ideas on how to hold the tower, but were worried that it might fall while this work was carried out.

The most popular idea was for a large concrete shaft to be built into the centre of the tower and extended deep into the ground. Then they would inject some concrete-like substance into the ground surrounding the tower to solidify the ground, thus supporting the tower. My idea was to construct three raking shores, linked together, from tubular scaffolding on the sinking side, with three platforms cantilevered around the tower at different levels to embrace the tower.

There had already been several ideas sent in which were on display nearby, mostly from young boys. One boy had suggested that they should build another tower beside the leaning tower and strap the two together. Another boy suggested that they should erect a very large fan beside the tower, blowing air at the tower while the work was carried out. Imagine working on the tower while a fan that size was blowing! Probably the best idea came from a boy of about eleven years old, who said they should dig a big hole under the high side at the base and let it fall back upright. Another lad suggested that they should build a huge statue of the original architect holding the tower upright.

Eventually they decided to dig the foundation out on the high side, by using computer-controlled drills to bring the tower back to a safe level. I sent my drawings to the authorities in Pisa and eventually got a reply saying "thanks but no thanks". After a couple of weeks sulking and licking my wounds at this rejection, and thinking it was their loss, I went back to looking for more modest work.

I went to contractors, always hoping that they might have some high level work that they might want to subcontract. Soon after the rejection of Big Ben and the Leaning Tower of Pisa, I was asked by one of the contractors to work on a large public school in Surrey. This school, built in the Gothic style from Bargate stone, with the quoins and features in deep pit Bath stone, was a really good example of the Bath and Bargate mix that was so popular in this area in the late Victorian period. This school was built in 1872 and with its bands of coloured clay tiles must have looked quite spectacular when first built; it is still very beautiful today.

All the towers to the different boarding houses have clay tiles with large cast iron finials, topped with classic flag weathervanes. The weathervanes are made from cast brass, very heavy for their size. Originally they were gilded and all the towers were fitted with cast iron gutters and downpipes. So when local contractors were on site decorating internally and were asked by the school to extend their contract to the outside of the building it seemed that they would have to scaffold each tower separately.

For the first one they got scaffolders to erect scaffolding around the tower and extend it up for the weathervane. We were asked to repair and paint the weathervane and finial, using their paint on the finial and metallic gold paint on the weathervane. We made the point that metallic gold paint would go dull in a very short time and the flags, at least, should be gilded. It seemed that they had overspent and the pot had run dry. This was when we suggested that on the next house they should forget conventional scaffolding and perhaps consider using our steeplejacks' methods on the exterior, saving a lot of money. The school agreed and we started work.

After a few days, the contractor who was working elsewhere on the school asked us if we could help him out. They were working on a tall chimney stack above a large gable, where they were trying to line one of the flues. They had scaffolding up to the base of the chimney and were trying to lower clay liners down the flue, but were not able to get down to fix the joint, which was a mortar joint. Always willing to help, I said we would have a look. They had got three sections fitted by joining them together and pushing them up the flue, but with every section they added it got harder and they were also fouling the rough interior of the flue. I told the contractor that we could help by lowering the sections from the top. We could joint them in situ and fill the space around the liners at the same time. We agreed a price and told him that we would do the job the following weekend.

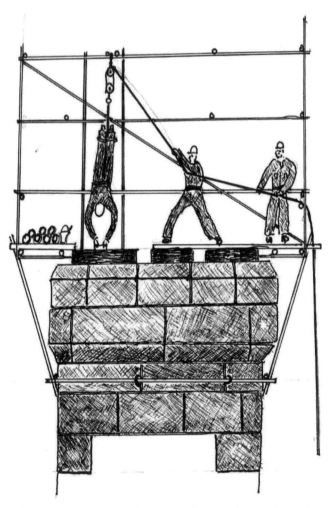

My plan was to extend the scaffolding above the chimney to form a head tree, fix a sheave block and lower a man down the flue. There was not a lot of room, so we suspended our shortest man by his ankles from this block and with him holding a section of the liner in front of himself we lowered him down the flue. We had a length of three inch plastic pipe which we ran down the corner beside him and after he had fixed a section of liner we could pour the infill down this pipe. When he shouted that a section was full, we hauled him up again and repeated the operation until all the liners were fitted.

After successfully lining the chimney for the contractor we returned to our own work on the school. This was the second house that we had worked on and this time we were using our steeplejack methods, which was creating a lot of interest at the school. Whereas on the first house everything had been scaffolded, this time we were using bosun's chairs. Although the school was extremely pleased with the savings they had made, they still insisted that we used metallic gold paint instead of gilding on the weathervane.

The school was a very good start to working on our own account, as over the next few years we worked on all their spires and towers. One of the most interesting jobs we had at this school was on the main tower, which is situated right at the centre of this very impressive set of buildings and towers above everything else. Again it is built from Bath and Bargate stone, with a large and heavily ornamented lead spire topped with a large cast iron finial that is embellished with beautiful copper leaves. Sadly again there is no gold, even though these had originally been gilded.

Access to the base of the spire is by ladders up the inside where there is a stone parapet on all four sides. From this parapet gutter it is ladder access to the apex. As there is no permanent fixing we had to lift some of the herringbone rolls to get a fixing. This main tower of the school looks impressive with its louvered openings, but in reality it is a water tower. The whole top of the tower is a huge still water tank and to reach the parapet you literally have to squeeze past. As we were fighting our way past this tank we noticed a lot of strings hanging off the outside of the tank. One of my men asked if I knew what or why they were doing there, but I had no idea. Eventually curiosity got the better of him. He pulled one of the strings, and to his surprise found three bottles of beer on the end. It seemed that this was the wine cooler for midnight parties.

This particular tower was to cause us more problems, as a few months later we were asked to carry out repair work externally. There appeared to be a problem with these very large louvered openings. We rigged up alloy track to the four sides of the tower, just above the Bath stone parapets. We had originally intended to rig from the parapets, but on close inspection we founds that the balustrading was too flimsy and of doubtful strength. From this alloy track we suspended single jockeys with bosun's chairs. From these chairs it was easy to walk along the complete elevation and also raise or lower yourself as required. This worked amazingly well until we tried to reach the louvred blades, which were set back some three feet from the face of the elevation. To reach these blades you needed to swing backwards and forwards until you could just reach one of the blades with your toe, then by holding yourself in you could fix a bowsing lanyard to hold yourself in to carry out the work.

Because of the need to move up and down a lot, we had rigged all the bosun's chairs with a Weston's purchase, which meant that to raise yourself one foot in height you had to pull three feet on the fall rope, and the opposite when lowering.

Generally we were using a stop lashing to hold us while working. But on this occasion, as we were swinging in and out and lowering, it was easier to wrap the fall rope around your leg. It saved a lot of time loosening and tightening the stop lashing and as we were just swinging in, treating the timber and swinging out again, wrapping the rope around your leg seemed easier, if not as safe.

On this occasion I was leaning, trying to reach the difficult corner, stretching out of my reach, when an unexpected gust of wind took me by surprise.

The thing you concentrate on in situations like this is not the hundred foot drop, it's not letting go of the paint.

Not having the stop lashing, before I could grab the rope I had dropped about six feet, which meant that eighteen feet of rough manila rope had rubbed across my shin and started to rub into the bone.

In traditional steeplejack's first aid, a bit of rag and some insulating tape should do the job. In this case it didn't. I still have problems with it over half a century later. A lesson learned the hard way.

But although it is hard to get work, if you are determined enough and do the job well you will always get work eventually.

Chapter Three

The Type of Men

Getting staff is always a difficult job, no matter what your occupation. People often say that it must be hard to get men to work at heights. Well, that doesn't seem to be the problem. The main problem is that in this job you can't always work near home and need to be willing to stay away all week.

The other problem is that the men seem to be great lovers and either fall in love with someone while we are away at work, and don't want to come home or move on to the next job, or they fall in love with a local girl and don't want to go away to work. It seems that a lot of the good men fall into this category. We as a company were lucky and had some very good men who stayed with us for many years, but we did employ quite a few more casual men over the years of very varied abilities.

At the time we were working on the public school in Surrey, we had taken on a new man who was of a very surly nature. One day there was just him and me at the school. We had just finished erecting our ladders up one of the taller towers, when this chap came over and introduced himself as the bursar. "Good morning Mr. Harknett", he said, "I understand that you are the most intrepid man in the South." The new man was standing right behind me and he growled in my ear: "Hit the bastard, Pete!" The bursar turned and walked away, I hoped that he hadn't heard. I turned to my mate and asked what that was all about. He said "I would never let anyone call me one of those". I explained that the bursar was paying me a compliment. He said it didn't matter and he'd still have hit the bastard.

Another young man we employed came down to Cornwall with us, met the only woman in the world for him and refused to come back with us when the job was finished. Three months later he turned up at the yard looking for his job back. It seemed that during his stay in Cornwall he'd met several girls who were the only one in the world for him and had been thrown out.

Another chap who was working for us up in Anglesey met this Sophia Loren lookalike and started dating her. On this particular job the weather was appalling and as we were working on a very high chimney stack the authorities at the plant often wouldn't let us climb. It seemed that they measured the wind force and only let us climb it below a certain level. This meant that on many days we would turn up for work only to be told that the wind was too strong and we should come back tomorrow. The Anglesey job must have been one of the worst jobs ever. We couldn't work when it was wet and they wouldn't let us work if it was windy. And it seemed as if it was always wet and windy.

Sometimes we had no work for days-- very boring when in lodgings. I often drove around the island, sketching to pass the time and not being too far away if the weather improved. On one occasion I was sitting in my car sketching the lighthouse.

It was really bucketing down and I had to keep my windscreen wipers on when suddenly, around the lighthouse came my mate and the Sophia Loren lookalike completely naked, holding hands and skipping. Perhaps the shower wasn't working in the digs.

On another occasion we had returned south again. We were laying a new roof on this village church. We were sitting on a grass bank near the lych gate when one of the men, a young lad really, asked me why I always went wandering around the churchyard whenever we arrived at a new church. He had noticed that I always wander around the churchyard during our lunch break. I explained to him that I was reading the gravestones and it is amazing how much local history you could learn from just reading the gravestones. How short people's lives were and how whole families were buried in the same churchyard, because people didn't travel far in those days. This explanation seemed to satisfy him and no more was said.

A few weeks later, we had just started work on another spire and I noticed that the lad had gone wandering around the churchyard. I never said anything as I thought he might learn something. The next day when we were having our lunch he wandered off again and when he returned he sat down, eating his lunch, looking very thoughtful. After a while he said to me: "You're right about how whole families are buried in the same churchyard. In this churchyard nearly every grave is the same family." He had read the same name on all the gravestones; they were all called "Sacred". He hadn't read the rest of the inscription ("to the memory of").

Another young man we had with us was on a job down in Cornwall. We were working on a church at Falmouth and staying in digs at Redruth. There was just me and this one young man doing the job. After work we would get a very good meal at the digs and after dinner I would read or watch

TV for a bit but my mate, being much younger, would borrow the van and go out. On this one occasion I had gone to bed when the contractor we were working for turned up a bit niggly and told me that my mate had got my van on the beach at St Agnes and that the tide was coming in.

I went with the contractor in his van. When we arrived I was horrified. My little van was right out near the water's edge, with the tide just turning. My mate was sitting on the bonnet looking out to sea, trying to look like King Canute. In the back of the van was a very slim girl in just a miniskirt and crop top. She looked frozen and not impressed with my mate. It was just luck that we had been working on a tall building and had a long rope, as the contractor refused to take his van on the beach. The rope was just long enough to reach my van. I took one end of the rope out with me, but the van had sunk and I had to dig my way under it. It was a slow, laborious job. Three times while I was wriggling under the van the young lady crept round the back of the van. I assumed she was sheltering from the wind. It was only after we had pulled the van onto safe ground that my mate told me she had drunk about eight pints of Guinness. It seems she was well known for it. On our wages he certainly could not afford her!

This same man and myself were working on a tower block for the military in Aldershot when the Ministry of Works sent a man down to the site to ask if we could go to the Duke of Wellington's statue, which was fairly close by. This very large statue of the duke in full military attire, sitting on a horse and surveying the surrounding area through a telescope standing on a large stone plinth, all on top of a large mound. This statue would be very difficult to climb without ladders etc., but obviously someone had – and it must have been done during the night. On the duke's telescope they had tied half a dozen balloons. They had lifted the feathers on his helmet so that he looked like Hiawatha and they had jammed a small pram onto his head. I think this must have been carried out over several nights.

We had to finish work on the tower block – it wasn't the sort of job you could just leave – so it was evening before we got to the statue, but it was summertime so it was still light. We started laddering up the plinth and up the horse's hind leg, then up the back of the duke himself. I was just about to remove the pram when the police turned up. They had been watching the statue and nobody had told them that we were coming. They called us down and put us in the back of their car for questioning. The first thing they asked was our names. I gave them mine but my mate said his name was Cliff. When they asked him "Cliff who?" he answered "Richard". I think they were having a long bad day, because they didn't think it was funny. As it was evening they couldn't get an answer from the Ministry of Works, but eventually I convinced them that we were removing the offending items. Some blokes just don't know when to keep quiet, but he was a good jack and stayed with us for a few years. And the duke got his feathers back in place.

One morning we were in a local builders' merchants, loading up with the help of a very small man who was looking very down in the dumps. I asked him what the problem was and he told me that he had worked as a jockey, but had lost his job and taken temporary work at the builders' merchants. He asked if we had any vacancies. I told him that our job was not everyone's cup of tea, but if he had a spare day he could come and work for us for the day. He would get a day's pay and he and I could decide if it would work.

The next day I picked him up from the agreed place. We were working on a church nearby, re-covering it with chestnut shingles and also gilding the sundial and weather vane, so I thought he might find it interesting. The other men had gone on earlier, so he would ride with me. And "ride" was certainly the operative word: as soon as the van started to move he half stood up in a sort of crouched position and kept bobbing up and down, holding imaginary reins as if he was riding a horse.

When we arrived at the job I didn't mention this strange behaviour to anyone, but told one of my men to show him what to do, carrying bundles of shingles around the back of the church. Quite a simple, straightforward task; pick up a bundle of shingles, put it on your shoulder and walk round the back-- not this fellow. He tied the bundle on his back and galloped round the back. When I asked him why he tied the shingles on to his back he said he needed both hands free to hold the reins.

At lunchtimes we used to go to a snack bar just up the road from the job. As I thought this fellow was probably short of cash I bought everyone a burger so that he wouldn't be embarrassed. These burgers were not very big but he, the new fellow, stuffed the whole burger into his mouth and ate it. I made some remark and he said "You ain't seen nothin' yet!" and promptly ordered four more which he ate at the same pace. At the end of the day I asked him how he had found the day. He said he had other jobs to try and would let me know. We never saw him again.

Chapter Four

The Job

As I mentioned earlier, there are many stories about repping. I was working in the Berkshire area and used to travel through a particular town most days and noticed that there were several problems with the clock dials on a very large stone spire. The dials were very heavy, made of cast iron. Several of the numbers and the frames had cracked and some parts had fallen off. The dials looked very unsafe.

This one morning I decided to stop and call in at the vicarage so I knocked at the door. The vicar opened and glared at me, very unfriendly. I explained who I was and told him about the clock dials. He listened for a while and then told me to clear off, saying he knew I was only after a handout and he did not give people money at the door.

About a week later, an architect I had worked for in the past rang me and asked if I could help him. A vicar had called him, worried about his church as he had had a very scruffy Irish vagrant using it as an excuse to ask for money, so would I visit and do an inspection of the tower and spire. A few days later, with my ladders and equipment, I knocked on the vicar's door again. I think this time he felt a little silly and embarrassed.

This was a very large Bath stone spire, sitting on top of a lofty dressed stone tower with a very heavy wrought iron finial. Most things were in very good condition. The finial only needed painting, but both the dials were cast iron and had fractured in several areas. The strange thing was that the gilding was still in remarkable condition and even after we had taken the dials to a blacksmith and remounted them, the gilding only needed repairing.

Another story about repping was down in Sussex, where a small spire on a church at the base of the Downs had a weather vane that was obviously in need of some attention. A colleague of mine had noticed this and as I had worked on a number of churches in the area I thought that the next time I was in the area perhaps I should call in, which I did.

Early one morning I called at the church. The vicarage was next door. I knocked and waited a few moments. All of a sudden, the door flew open and there was the vicar wearing the tiniest pair of knickers. I could hardly believe my eyes – little white knickers decorated with little red hearts. I explained that I wanted to examine his spire, but needed the key. He gave me a huge smile and said, "Come in!"

I said I would rather wait at the door. He turned and flounced down the passage. The back view was far worse than the front. We got the job done and posted the keys back through the letter box. A few weeks later we went back and repaired his weather vane. This time he was wearing a cassock, or perhaps it was a frock. I imagine that the first time we called was on his day off and he was relaxing.

A lot of the stories about repping are not always from cold calling. Often when asked by architects or a Diocesan Advisory Committee (DAC) to visit a church you still get a frosty reception when you turn up at the vicarage. One such occasion was in South Kensington, where they were having problems with their roof. This roof was particularly difficult to get to without an awful lot of scaffolding. Someone who knew someone had asked the Guildford DAC who had recommended me. So one morning I turned up at the church. It was not like an ordinary church; it looked more like a block of flats. There was no south door with a porch, or anything that looked the slightest bit churchy. I settled on the most impressive door on the street, a very strong-looking oak door with a small opening with bars. I looked more like a prison door, in fact Newgate's knocker came to mind.

I began to wonder if I had got the right place, but the address seemed right so I banged the huge knocker and after what seemed like an age the little door behind the bars slid sideways. The head of a nun appeared and said, "Yes?"

I explained that I was expected and ask if she could tell the reverend gentleman that I was here. She started muttering about how you could not trust anyone and all they wanted was your money and your body. They would beat you up if they got the chance and steal and abuse you – and no, she wouldn't open the door to someone like me. Eventually I persuaded her to at least go to the reverend and tell him I was there. She slammed the little door shut and I waited for what seemed like an age.

She came back and opened the little door, still muttering about how they only want your body or your money and how the father was wrong to tell her to open the door, but after a little wait I heard the bolts going back. Now that I'd told her my name and she'd spoken to the reverend, who had said I was okay, she still kept muttering away about me wanting money, but she opened the door and said, "You had better come with me, Mr. Thug". Now that the door was open I could see her. She was less than five foot tall, well into her eighties, humped back and using a stool to reach the many bolts. After talking to the priest we were asked to do the job, which turned out to be very pleasant and successful. But we did make our own access up the outside.

Soon after we had finished that job we had an enquiry from an architect, a member of a practice in Wiltshire. He was the inspecting architect for a stone church. There was a lot of damp to the upper parts of the tower. There was parapet gutter where he thought the problem was, but as there was no access, perhaps we could help.

We arrived at the church with our ladders etc. and were surprised that a tower of this size had no access from the ground. We could see no obvious signs that there ever had been. We laddered up the outside and when we reached the parapet we were amazed. The gutter behind the parapet was about two feet wide and around three feet deep. It was completely full of pigeon droppings, dead birds and leaves. Nobody had been up here for many years.

We laddered up the spire, fixed ropes and tackles and started the long and laborious job of lowering the muck down. We rigged our gantline to lower the muck down to a paved area near the vestry door. We set up some boards to form a large box that would contain the muck in a tidy heap as we would hire a skip later in the job. We started work lowering, but very soon the box was overflowing and beginning to get a bit messy. But we kept sweeping it into a heap, leaving access to the vestry.

About mid-morning we were working away, lowering the muck, laughing and joking and telling each other exaggerated stories about the weekend, when the vicar suddenly appeared by the vestry door and shouted up, very irate and cross about something. He called me down and as I was climbing down wondering what we had done wrong, he came over to the ladders and I noticed he had very dirty and hands and his face was all black and dusty. I thought he must have been cleaning in the church. He was obviously very angry. He said that he could hear us talking and laughing even when he was in his vestry and that the language was disgusting and the subjects even worse. This was a church, so could we tone it down a bit and change the subject. I told him I was sorry and would speak to the men. I climbed back up and told the men. They were surprised that he could hear us, as he had shut himself in the vestry. As it was about tea time I suggested that we go round to the area we had cleared and have a cup of tea out of our flasks.

The area we had cleared was above the vestry roof in the corner of the parapet. There was an old chimney built into the stone work, standing about three feet above the parapet coping stones. As everything was rather messy, we drank our tea leaning against the spire and parapet. Nobody fancied sitting down. One of our chaps leaned back against the chimney and it toppled over, dropping down and crashing through the vestry roof.

The vicar, who had obviously had his head in the fireplace listening (which would explain the dirty face), shot out of the door at close to 100 mph. He slipped and shot straight into our huge pile of revolting pigeon muck. He was buried almost up to his armpits. He looked up to us looking down over the parapet, shook his fist and let out a stream of abuse that made us doubt our parentage and taught us some new swear words. That vicar had no right to tell me about our language.

It is strange how one job can lead to another. We were working on a large stone church in West Sussex. This church has a massive Norman tower with a tiled pyramidal roof. It has had quite a chequered history. Originally the tower was capped with a herringbone lead spire. This was replaced by a stone broached spire during the Victorian era. By the 1930s this became unsafe and was dismantled down to the broach level. It stayed that way during the war years, then in the early 1950s it was decided not to rebuild the spire but to cap the tower with the roof we see today – a great pity. I think they got it wrong. Recognising that they didn't want to spend a lot of money strengthening the ageing stone tower, they should have built a much lighter spire in the Sussex duck's foot broach style clad in locally produced chestnut shingles. This I feel would have been correct for the area and, sitting on top of the hill, would have rivalled the local cathedral.

However, I digress. We were repairing some of the stone work to the tower when one lunchtime a builder pulled up in his van. He had been watching us working on ropes and wondered if we could help him. He was working on a house nearby and had lifted the kitchen floor and found this very large hole. He wanted one of us to go down, just to satisfy his curiosity. We took a long rope and followed him back to the site.

When we arrived I was very surprised that this house was built on the side of a very steep hill. The hill swept down to a stream running through the valley. That put paid to my first thought that it was probably an old well, as with the water table that far below it, it would have required a rope of great length to have reached water, and the spindle to wind the rope would have been huge. When we looked down the hole, which was a very rough shape, very irregular, more like a natural fault in the hill, but there were very badly rusted pitons so somebody had been down or had climbed up from an opening far below.

I had heard somewhere that if you drop a lighted flame down a shaft and it burns, the air is pure and there is oxygen. So we rolled up a page of newspaper, lit it and dropped it down the hole. It fluttered down until it burnt out. I lowered myself down to the level where the paper had burnt out and shone a torch down. I could still see nothing but a big black hole, so I lit another sheet of paper and watched as it fluttered on down. Safe to go lower, I descended to where the paper had burnt out and shone my torch down again – still just a big black hole. By this time I was about 40 feet below the kitchen floor. I hung there, looking around for some indication of what this hole was about. I looked at the rusting pitons and in my opinion they had been put in by someone climbing up.

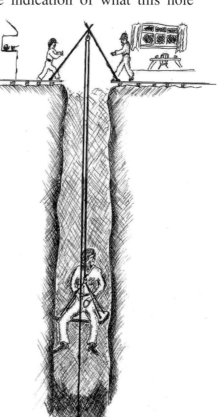

I slowly pulled myself up. It was hard work, as I couldn't get any purchase with my feet.

When I eventually reached the kitchen floor, very out of breath and puffing well, I told the builder my view that it was probably a fault in the soft sandstone and that someone or something had climbed up from an opening far below, perhaps before the house was built. The builder decided that as it would cost money to get it properly surveyed he wouldn't bother; he would just put a concrete slab over it and forget all about it. I occasionally think about it and wonder if whoever lives there now realises that a few inches below their feet there is a very deep hole that someone or something had climbed up and perhaps that funny unexplained noise they hear some evenings is something knocking. We left it to the builders and went back to the truncated church where we spent several weeks repairing the stonework in beautiful surroundings.

As I mentioned earlier, you can specialise in one part of the craft but you have to accept work in all aspects of the job. Probably the most dangerous of all our work is demolition. Most of the demolition that steeplejacks are asked to do is knocking down old factory chimney stacks.

Basically there are three ways of demolishing chimneys. One is to cut out the bottom brickwork about two thirds of the way around the base of the chimney and shore it up with stout timbers. Then pack the openings with inflammable materials, set it on fire and wait for it to fall. The safest and quickest way is to blow the base out with explosives, but that's not always possible when there are other properties nearby. The third way is known as working on the wall. The steeplejack knocks a large hole in the bottom of the stack, erects a small platform near the top then stands on the chimney brickwork, knocks off a course of bricks and lets them fall down the inside of the stack where the rubble can be retrieved through the hole at the bottom.

According to legend there is another method, which if true is certainly the cheapest. This is known as the penny cane method. This method requires at least two men. One man, using a compressed air breaker, starts cutting the brickwork at the base of the chimney (I imagine that they take this part in turns) and after they have got some of the way around, and while the chimney is still safe, they jam a bamboo cane between the upper brickwork and the base. They visually line this up with some upright object and while one carries on breaking out bricks the other one watches the cane and as soon it starts to bend they run like hell. I have only read about this method and have never tried it.

Chapter Five

Shingles

Next I would like to give a brief history of shingles and their use in this country. The first known use of cleft timber as a roof covering was in Roman times, but I am sure that cleft timber has been used since the time of the early metal tools. It seems that the Romans used cleft timber on their more primitive buildings, like workmen's shelters, stables and woodsmen's huts, or any structure that was considered temporary. With their relatively short life, none have survived.

I feel that the Saxons probably used cleft timber quite extensively, but it was not until the Normans arrived that there is any real evidence. The Normans are well known for their powerful building, with very thick-walled church towers that are very large on plan but not too tall. But I believe that the Normans looked at our Saxon buildings and builders very carefully, and if you look closely at some of the work attributed to the Saxons I think it was built by the Normans, who were using some of the Saxons' great ideas and practices.

Generally speaking the idea of the Normans using Saxon ideas and practices seems to rest solely with me. I can't recall anybody else subscribing to the idea but I believe that the Normans and the Saxons probably stole or borrowed each other's ideas though they did it furtively – just the same as steeplejacks did before the founding of the Federation of Master Steeplejacks in 1948. In those days it was not uncommon to be standing on top of a chimney or church spire with binoculars peering at another jack who was peering at you from another job a mile or so away. If an important job was about to start or had just started as you approached the village or town, you would often see a ladder-loaded van in a layby with a pair of binoculars poking out of the window. The only difference is that binoculars have improved enormously!

I like to look at the probability rather than the lack of hard evidence as people don't seem to change over the years. They have always altered buildings to make them look more up to date as the fads and fashions change so when looking for evidence, you must try to get back to the original or whatever remains of it. There is one such church where the tower is obviously of Norman origin, although the top section has been rebuilt and altered over the years. The base of the tower is built of massive stones, with long and short quoins all laid horizontally making this a very strong base, the only one I have found yet.

On all these massive buildings there were workmen who started as boys, became tradesmen and spent their whole working lives on single buildings. Between the buttresses (and there were many) they built so-called temporary tradesmen's shelters. It would make sense to have covered those with cleft timber. The first shelters probably had just split boards, but as board could be used elsewhere on the building it made good sense to use all the small offcuts. These would have been the earliest English shingles.

It seems there was no uniform size until the mid-1600s, when there was a lot of church building and alterations. There seemed to be a lot of steeples being built on Norman towers. I believe that the Normans tried to build spires on their towers, but had used stone and started by springing them from inside the parapets. That worked well on the cardinal elevations, where the weight is transferred straight to the footing, and as they built the spires from the inside of the walls there was very little springing load. However, across what are known today as the broach elevations, there was little support. It seems that the Normans had not thought about corbelling, squinch arches, dragon beams etc. and most of their spires fell down.

In the late sixteenth century it seems that a lot of Norman churches were having timber spires erected on the very wide Norman towers. The builders overcame the problem by using massive timbers to form a cruciform, but more often formed a grillage of timber across the opening and broaching the spire. Broaching entails turning a spire from square to octagonal, overcoming the need for squinches etc. These very elegant and graceful structures became known as the Sussex duck's foot spire, because if you look at the inverted triangle that is the broach it looks very like a giant duck's foot. Most of these spires are very large and tall, because the builders were going to use local timber and needed the spire to be steep enough to drain quickly and not be too heavy. Although the tower walls with their mighty buttresses were strong enough, the cruciform or timber grillage was not, and needed a covering that was lightweight but durable.

After they had pitched the spire, they covered the complete structure with thin oak boarding, which was either cleft by hand or pit-sawn. I expect there were arguments about the use of boarding over the standard roof, which used oak or chestnut laths. They got it right by using boarding to obtain rigidity against the winds. This boarding made a very good substrate for the shingle covering.

Shingles by this time were mostly made off site, in estate woodland, by coppicing woodmen or in timber yards. They were made in various sizes at first. It is easier to cleave a shorter piece of timber, but shingles need to be long enough for there to be three layers. Clay roofing tiles were being laid in 4" gauge, so shingles needed to be 12" long. Similar considerations apply to width: a narrow piece of timber will cleave more easily, but for a roof to be watertight there needs to be a good side lap. Over time, 4" came to be the minimum width for a shingle.

It would seem that by the late sixteenth or early seventeenth century shingles were being made almost to a standard size, but thickness seemed to vary from maker to maker. I feel this was due to the availability of suitable oak. A maker working for a large estate had almost unlimited timber at his disposal, but a small coppice man had to buy all his timber and needed to get as many shingles as possible out of each cube.

The very early shingles were fixed with oak or chestnut

pegs known as tree nails. It must have been a very slow and laborious job. After offering up a shingle you would have to shape it with your axe, hold it in position, use a hand drill to bore a hole through the shingle and into the board behind it, drive in the hand-cleft tapered peg until the end you are hitting burrs over, then move on to the next shingle. This method of fixing was used up until the very early nineteenth century when they started using handmade nails.

These nails were made from copper or iron until the mid-nineteenth century, when zinc and zinc-coated nails started to appear. These nails all failed because of the acid that leaches from new oak shingles. Around the end of the nineteenth century most had returned to handmade copper, only by now they had appreciated that acid was destroying most of the nails so they increased the gauge.

Around 1900 oak was becoming very expensive and very scarce and coppice woodmen were making more fencing, which was much easier work than shingle making. About this time architects were reading about cedar shingles being used widely in Canada and America to great effect, with their long life expectancy, excellent insulating qualities and very attractive appearance. All this, and their very light weight made very interesting reading. By the 1920s timber importers were bringing in large enough quantities to make cedar a viable roof and wall covering. Architects started to design buildings for this new, lightweight covering.

In 1939 a pavilion was built for a school in the Surrey hills. It is attributed to the well-known architect Edwin Landseer Lutyens but I believe it was more likely to have been his son, Robert. The roof of this pavilion was certainly designed for clay tiles and I believe it was Robert Lutyens who probably read about the new shingles and thought, "I'll show Daddy." He would have done better if he'd listened to Daddy, as the pavilion has now had its third covering of cedar shingles. In this case I think they should have stayed with the clay tiles.

It wasn't until after the war that cedar was used on church spires in any quantity. One of the first spires to be covered with the new cedar shingles was Brookland on Romney Marsh. This is a strangely shaped spire built in layers, making it look more like a Christmas tree. It was built beside the church and is adorned with a flag weathervane – with many large bullet holes, courtesy of the Battle of Britain.

This was early days with cedar shingles in England and the strange spire at Brookland was covered at that time with shiplap boarding in the style of a smock mill. This boarding was causing some problems and needed treating regularly, being so near the sea, so somebody had the idea of covering it with cedar shingles. They decided to leave the shiplap boarding and nail the cedar shingles directly onto the shiplap. Shiplap is not a constant thickness, so some of the nails had very poor purchase. This weakness in the fixings meant that it needed constant maintenance, but the shingles lasted well, as it was not reshingled until a few years ago.

During the 1960s and '70s almost every timber spire was re-covered with cedar shingles. Colts of London had started to tanalise them and were supplying bronze nails with their shingles, but unfortunately others were supplying aluminium nails. Some were coated with lanolin to protect against acid runoff, but the aluminium nails proved to be a complete failure.

Right up until the Great Storm of 1987 the bulk of all church spires were covered with cedar shingles, although there had been a movement to use hand-cleft chestnut that was mainly backed by Colts of Havant. Most of their shingles came from France but Colts did try, with the help of Sam Ford (a local woodsman) to produce their own.

The French sweet chestnut shingles were very good with dimensions very similar to the traditional English shingle. We drilled and fixed a lot of these French shingles, using stainless steel nails. Altogether we re-covered 15 to 20 spires around the South with chestnut. Chestnut shingles are blocked, i.e. the tree is cut into 12" drums and then split straight across the drum and not on the quarter, as with oak, so there is always some sapwood on the edge of each shingle, even after careful trimming. This sapwood rots out long before the hardwood, leaving bigger gaps between the shingles and reducing the side lap coverage.

After the Great Storm (a non-existent hurricane according to one weather forecaster) fifteen million trees had fallen. A large percentage of these were oak. A lot had fallen on or near roads. These were easily recovered and were of course snapped up by timber merchants for planking etc., but the trees that had fallen in less accessible places were far too expensive for them to recover. We could cut and split these trees into manageable pieces.

We purchased a lorry and a small powered tracked trailer and recovered some of this timber. For very little money we stacked hundreds of tons on our land, trained a couple of men and started making shingles.

We sold some of the shingles to others at a very reasonable price, but used most ourselves. This was really the start of oak shingles being used again.

Chapter Six

The Problems

There are very few problems with shingles on church spires and if fixed properly they should stay unattended for their expected life, which is approximately 70 years for sawn cedarwood or around 100 years for hardwood: oak or chestnut.

Other timbers have been tried. Pine, for example, which was supplied smoked, or elm which was cleft very young, or a variety of African hardwood. But all these brought more problems. The main problem is bad fixing. Architects and specifiers looking at a spire are well trained in general building practices but need the advice of a specialist when facing the unusual. The problem is knowing where to go for that specialist advice. If they enquire of a building or roofing contractor and ask whether they have men who are trained in this work, the stock-in-trade answer will be, "Yes, of course we do."

These contractors believe that a church spire is exactly the same as any other roof and don't like to admit that their men are not trained for this work. What they do not appear to understand is that church spires are usually high and very exposed. They are also a very unusual shape and have many problems that a conventional roof does not. I am sure that the majority of experienced roofers and builders are excellent tradesmen, who with the advantage of a one day course in church spire shingling could carry out an excellent job.

Other than the fixing, the main problem with shingled spires is woodpeckers, which have always been a problem on timber spires. They peck holes at the top of the vertical joints where the timber is at its thinnest and leave a small hole about half an inch in diameter. These holes often get enlarged by squirrels, who like to build their drays inside spires. Once the hole is large enough, you get birds inside. Contrary to popular belief, the woodpeckers do not want to set up home inside the spire. They leave that to the other birds and squirrels. All the woodpecker is interested in are the flies and insects who live under the shingles.

There will always be a difference of opinions as to why the woodpecker pecks holes in the shingle covering. Some say they are drumming for a mate, but if this is the case then they don't seem to be very successful. Others say they are only feeding and I agree with this latter view, as the problem is getting very much worse since the loss of the insects' habitats. The biggest contributor seems to be the tragic loss of our beautiful majestic elm trees.

As the problem of the woodpeckers grows, so do the ideas to tackle it. The answer really is to shingle well, appreciating the woodpeckers' needs, but there are many who have applied their minds to the problem. One solution, suggested by someone who has never been near a church spire, was to spread peanut butter over the whole spire. The theory behind this was that the person knew woodpeckers don't like peanut butter.

Another idea was to fix model birds of prey on the spire to frighten the woodpeckers away. They didn't.

One architect, a church repairing expert, suggested that we fix very thin stainless steel wires down the whole length of the spire, from the apex to the eave, at three foot intervals at the eaves and converging at the apex. The idea was that the birds would not see these wires, would hit their wings on them and be frightened into flying away. They did see the wires and weren't frightened away. He had underestimated the birds' eyesight.

One wise lady architect from Kent, who had a lot of experience in shingling church spires, agreed that the woodpeckers were in fact only looking for a good dinner and saved their more romantic activities for more discreet areas in the woods. She suggested that we layer zinc between the courses in the vulnerable areas of a spire. i.e. the tops of the broaches, the hollow areas behind the concave above the eaves, and at the apex. We tried this method with good results, but the canny birds then started attacking other areas where there might not be so many insects but the pickings were still better than nothing. We developed this idea further and fixed stainless steel behind the shingles on every course. This stopped the woodpeckers completely and is still the only way to guarantee that a spire is woodpecker proof. Today we are using and recommending traditional oak shingles, which if manufactured and laid correctly certainly seem to be the answer. We have been laying these shingles, or having other people lay them under strict supervision, for the last fifteen years with no woodpecker problems.

After we had used up all the timber we had collected from the storm of 1987, we looked for another supplier but found it was nearly impossible to get anyone to produce shingles to an acceptable standard. One of the last spires we used our own shingles on was St Mary and All Saints at Dunsfold, which is a pretty little church some miles from the actual village. The tower is shingled with decorated shingles and the spire is a small Sussex duck's foot broached spire. We carried out this work as part of a major restoration project for the main contractors, AE Hughes of Leatherhead, all under the very strict supervision of architect John Deal, a firm but fair man with a good knowledge of shingling. Under his supervision we won the Worshipful Company of Carpenters "Wood Award" for conservation.

Soon after this job we could find no woodsmen who were interested in manufacturing shingles to our specification in any quantity. However a shingle maker in the Bavarian Forest, Germany, who we had done business with in the past, was very keen to produce as many as we required and supply them through West & Sons of Sussex.

Another problem we have is teaching men which way they are facing, although as most of our work is on Christian churches they really shouldn't have any trouble.

One such instance was when we were working on a large church in the Surrey hills. We had a new fellow who was just beginning to learn steeplejacking and was a little nervous. We had just finished erecting a small platform at the top of this spire when he decided to try and climb up and have a look at the view. He slowly climbed, stopping for a blow and to steady his nerves, eventually reaching the top hanging on like a cobweb. After he had climbed over the handrail he started to relax and take in the splendid view. We were standing admiring the view, looking north, when he said, "This is fantastic – I can see the Eiffel Tower." I followed his gaze and could see the Crystal Palace mast in the distance, I had to explain that we were looking north and Paris is not north of Surrey.

These days we always blame the woodpeckers for the problems with shingles. Although it is not always them, they certainly are responsible for a large proportion of the holes in spires, which squirrels enlarge. But jackdaws can also be a serious problem. One spire we were asked to re-shingle in Hampshire was covered in hand-cleft oak shingles which still had several years' life left in them, but there was a problem up near the apex. Approximately six feet down from the lead capping there were four lead-covered spire lights, where a very large family of jackdaws were living. These jackdaws had lived in the top of this spire for many years and over those years steeplejacks had climbed up and put a variety of meshes over the openings, but it seems they had always got back in.

As we were going to be completely re-covering the spire, we were asked to pay extra care to these spire lights. We spent the next couple of weeks stripping and reshingling. We were using tanalised cedar shingles, as at time there really was nothing else available. There were no problems with woodpeckers. We were treating the timbers with a contact poison (allowed in those days) and laying the shingles in very small courses so we were confident of a good job. When we reached the height of the spire lights, we opened up the spire to get the jackdaws out. We managed to get a small man inside and he started to throw out the nest and the corpses of the jackdaws' grandparents. He was amazed at how deep this nest was. By the time he got down to the base and could measure the distance from the spire lights down to the cruciform where the nest had started, he had removed 26 feet of jackdaw nest. We have all heard stories of jackdaws picking up anything that glitters, but we didn't find anything of value. In fact, over the years all I have ever found glittering in jackdaw nests have been a few aluminium milk bottle tops.

After clearing out this nest and treating the timbers, we rebuilt the spire lights and recovered them with lead. I thought the specification for the lead was far too light, but the architect insisted – he knew best – and we carried on. After a couple of days we had finished work on the spire lights. We sealed the openings with stainless steel mesh and went home for the weekend. On Monday morning we returned to the site and on climbing up to the spire lights were amazed to find that the jackdaws had pecked holes right through the lead and had tried to pull it off, making a real old mess. We had to replace all the lead with much heavier sand-cast lead which, left to our own devices, is the type and weight we would have used in the first place. Because of the jackdaw problem, we returned eighteen months later to inspect the spire lights. We climbed up and found everything to be in order. Even though jackdaws are very determined birds, they know when they are beaten.

Chapter Seven

Industrial Work

As I have mentioned earlier, to start with you take any jobs offered. I spent a couple of years on my own going around the South mostly, painting steel chimneys on nurseries, factories, laundries etc., occasionally pointing and repairing brick on any building that was difficult to access. On some of these structures I got asked back to demolish them. I sometimes wonder if I got the repairs wrong.

On one job, an old brickworks, I had spent several weeks pointing and repairing their chimneys, over a period of years, when suddenly they called it a day and closed their doors. I was asked to demolish two of the chimneys. There were three in total, but the tallest had to come down at a specific time as it was situated next to a main railway line so they got an explosives expert to drop it. One of the other two I could drop by cutting the base and burning, but the last one was in the middle of some buildings that were being kept, so this one had to come down the hard way. I decided to do this at weekends when there wouldn't be so many people about.

I had cut a hole in the bottom and asked a mate to help me at the weekend. He wanted to bring his young son to work. I agreed, as long as he sat in the van. All the mate had to do was clear the bricks away when I shouted down. I was standing on the top of the chimney, just having a blow or lighting my pipe, when I thought I saw something move down in the chimney. Thinking it was an animal, I went down and found my mate's son sitting in the opening. His dad had gone to the toilet and he had left the van. That could have been an early end to my career!

Sometime after this a mate and I decided to go up North looking for work and got a job working as scaffolders on some very large cooling towers. When we arrived on site they were looking for men to work on one of the towers that was about three quarters finished. Usually they liked men to start when the tower started and work their way up, but several men had left and these were the only vacancies going.

These towers are massive: about a thousand feet around the base and three hundred and seventy-five feet tall when finished. Cooling towers are not scaffolded in the conventional way but have brackets bolted through the wall with one lift of boards outside and a couple of lifts internally, all moved up as construction progresses. In the centre of the tower, scaffolding goes all the way up. Within this scaffold are passenger and material hoists. It was a great feeling, going up in the passenger hoist in these strangely shaped structures.

When we reached the working level, in this case about 200 feet up, there was no hanging about. Everyone was in a hurry as they were paid based on the amount of concrete poured. Because the towers are so large, the job is worked in two halves: while the concrete men are pouring one half, the scaffolders are raising the scaffold on the other half.

While we were working up on this tower we ran short of

some special fixings and someone needed to go down in the passenger hoist to ground level and get them. I was volunteered. I was okay with that and went to the hoist, but for some reason it wouldn't work and after hitting the "down" button several times I gave up and was told that the hoist was temperamental. Maybe that's why I was volunteered (as the new boy). There was ladder access, but it was a long way down through all that scaffolding. Very close to the passenger hoist was the material hoist.

The difference between a passenger hoist and a material hoist is that the passenger hoist winds up and down on a rack and pinion under very strict control, whereas a material hoist winds up with a winch. When the material hoist ascends, the winch winds up a wire onto a drum. But when it is lowered the operator eases off the brake and lets the platform (or in this case the concrete bucket) drop, powered by gravity.

Not fancying the climb down through the scaffolding to the ground, I looked at the material hoist. The man who operated it was on the lift above. I waited until he was distracted and jumped into the bucket. I had just got in and lowered myself out of sight when I heard him return and release the brake.

The bucket dropped like a stone. It was accelerating faster than I was, so that my backside was hovering above the bottom of the bucket. It only took a few seconds, but it was long enough for me to pray and regret getting in. The hoist operator must have been very good at his job. He stopped the bucket very gently, about a foot from the ground. I climbed out, shaking like a leaf.

Both my mate and I stayed working on this tower until it was almost completed when he decided to move on. But I stayed with the company. They asked if I would work on the chimney stack, which would be over six hundred feet tall when completed and had reached a height of between four and five hundred feet at that point. I had met a couple of men already, having had a drink or two with them in the wet canteen.

At that time there was a small hoist up the inside of the chimney with some scaffolding, but outside there was none. At the top there was timber shuttering around the stack, inside and out, and on the inside there was scaffolding from which men could fix the reinforcing and pour the concrete. Outside, there were small brackets bolted to the shuttering with scaffolding board splayed around to fix the shuttering. After the concrete had set, the bolts could be undone and the shuttering lifted off.

This really was a grand place to work on a fine day, but a bit bleak when the wind was blowing. One man, who was from Glasgow and had a very broad accent, was very fond of his party trick. Whenever a new person arrived at the top he would stand on the edge of the shuttering facing toward the centre and also facing the new person, who was usually a little uneasy. Then as he was talking he would fall backwards, screaming. The new fellow usually started to panic, shouting for help, before the Scotsman would climb back up and say "That was a near one." It would take the new fellow a little while to realise that there was a safety net a few feet below, right round the stack, about 15 feet wide. It may have been safe, but the Scot was the only one to do this.

While working on this chimney I had noticed a steel ladder running down one side of the stack. I assumed this was to give access to aircraft lights. It wasn't a ladder in the accepted sense, but was a series of stirrups (often called staples) about a foot apart. While we were working there was a strict rota for tea breaks. The hooter would go at ten o'clock and then again twenty minutes later. Everyone would scramble to get down to the tea room, get their food and drink and be back up by the time the second hooter sounded.

Thinking that I was "smarter than the average bear, Boo Boo!", I decided that ten minutes before the hooter sounded I would climb down these stirrups and would be down at ground level just as the hooter sounded, be first in the queue, get my sandwich and climb back up. Clever stuff! So the next day I kept my eye on the time and at ten minutes to ten, I started down these stirrups. I got to about a hundred feet from the ground when I suddenly ran out of ladder. For some reason there were no stirrups on the first hundred feet of the chimney.

So back up the ladder, in time to reach working level just as the hooter sounded to mark the end of tea break. No food or drink: very clever!

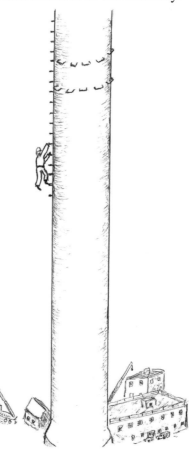

One evening, sitting in the wet canteen having a drink with a couple of older chimney men, they explained that when the chimney was finished there would be access up the inside and men would climb down the stirrups to maintain the aircraft lights so there was no need for a lower ladder. They also told me that I was not the first one to do what I had done, although usually it was them who suggested it to the newcomer.

I'd been to this canteen on the first day that I arrived on this site, during the daytime when they were not serving any alcohol. We were sitting having a cup of tea and chatting about our work. Whenever you start a new job, someone asks what work you have done and what sites you have worked on. When a very large Irishman came over and asked me to stand up I thought for one minute that I was in trouble, but I stood up anyway and he wrapped his huge arms around me and kissed me on both cheeks. I didn't recognise him at first, and he was far too big for me to hit, but he soon explained that we'd met at Dungeness power station where he claimed that I had saved his life. That of course was a huge exaggeration, but it was great to see him back at work and looking very fit.

He promptly started to tell everyone in the canteen how a few years before we were both working on the nuclear power station, he as a scaffolder and me as a rigger. We had never met, but were walking across a floor with a gang of other men. There were several large openings in this concrete floor that had been covered temporarily with sheets of shuttering plywood. Several of the men had walked over this particular sheet of plywood without a problem but when this very heavy Irishman stepped on it, it broke and he fell through.

There was about a hundred foot drop to the floor below where they were erecting a birdcage of scaffolding, so there were many poles sticking up. It doesn't bear thinking about. The man managed to grab hold of the edge of the opening. Everyone seemed to panic and run in every direction. I felt like running, too, but I grabbed an old piece of ladder that was nearby, tied the ladder to a piece of shuttering four-by-two and dangled the ladder down the hole so he could put a foot on one of the rungs, taking the weight from his hands. By then the others had come back and we hauled him out. He was very shaken up and went straight down to the office and jacked. He went back to Ireland and stayed for six months until he felt confident enough to return to this sort of work. Even after this encounter I never knew his name.

It was soon after this, while still working at Dungeness, that we had a visit from the law. Apparently someone had scaled the old lighthouse and had drained and stolen the mercury from under the light. The police were of the opinion that only people who had worked on a lighthouse would know that the light floats on a trough full of mercury and how to drain it out. Mercury is a very strange liquid metal and needs careful handling. After a lot of questions we convinced them that we had nothing to do with it. They had checked with Trinity House for the names of any steeplejacks who had worked for them.

About this time I set up on my own, but I still needed to work for other people as well. While searching for work I had an enquiry from a firm of painting contractors who had been asked to paint the top of a large concrete chimney. Often the tops of these concrete stacks are painted black – a sort of smoke ring, usually around the top ten feet or so. They were happy to do the job but weren't sure about access, so they asked me to go and look at the job with a view to me supplying the access.

I arrived at the site where there were several other people all looking at the same job. I was surprised just how big the chimney was – more a job for specialists than painting contractors. As the chimney was already laddered up outside, all secured to permanent fixing, I decided I would measure it up for them. At least that way I'd get a day's pay. There was another chap who was planning to do the same thing, climb and measure the job for his firm, so we decided to climb it together.

We started climbing, me going first and him following. After we'd climbed about 30 feet or so we legged in and had a blow, then climbed again and had another blow. We repeated this many times until we were about six feet from the top. It was only then that we realised the top six feet of ladder was missing.

We legged in and thought about it for a while, then decided I would go first. I was the longer man and this was definitely a long man job.

I found that by standing one rung down I could just reach the rim, after which I could steady myself while I climbed into the top rung and then onto the cups of the sleeves at the tops of

the stiles. I could then reach and get a good grip on top of the rim and, being a fit young man (back then), I could scramble up on top quite easily. But my climbing companion, who was a lot shorter than me, couldn't reach so I had to reach down, grab his hand and pull him up.

We both sat there for a while, getting our breath back, admiring the view and looking at the people far below us. We then got up and walked around the rim. This was a multi-flue chimney that was not completed and had no roof around or between the flues, so we had to be careful not to fall down either the inside or the outside. As we were shuffling our way around, discussing what method of fixings our firms would need to provide access outside, a helicopter arrived and nearly blew us off the stack. In it was a young man with a camera, waving at us. We waved back, but didn't use as many fingers.

Normally, when you are on top of one of these large diameter chimneys you can look around and see your ladder sticking up above the rim. In this case you couldn't, so you walk a few paces then peer over the side until you find the ladder, then comes the process of getting onto the ladder. It is always much easier to climb up than it is to climb down. We agreed-- long man first. I wriggled over the side feet first, on my stomach. I found it quite unnerving, hanging there trying to find the ladder with my feet. But I did and felt a lot better.

Then came the awkward bit. These ladders are a foot away from the wall and I was standing on the second rung down, with my large heavy bottom sticking out, knowing that I had to let go of the chimney rim – a very hairy few seconds. After I had gone down another couple of rungs the other little chap came over, but he couldn't quite reach the ladder. So I had to reach up, put my hand on his bottom and hold him against the wall while he slid down to the ladder. He seemed happy but I was glad the helicopter had gone. It was then just an easy climb down. Neither of us got the job.

On my way home after a hard day's work as I was driving down the hill into Rogate I looked over at the South Downs and Butser like I always did and saw the old brickworks chimney standing proudly, the top two feet or so showing above the trees. I always wondered how many had used it as a land mark before the day of good roads and signposts. Although I had looked out for it so many times on my journey home I had never been up to the old brick yard or had a good look at it from a distance through binoculars; something all steeplejacks did in the old days.

It was only when the Federation of Master Steeplejacks was formed in 1948 that steeplejacks started talking to each other and found by talking face to face that they had so much in common. Before this as they were driving around the country if they saw ladders fixed to a chimney or church spire they would pull up and out would come the binoculars and the mutterings started of how they were doing it all wrong.

This was soon to change as on one Sunday I received a phone call from the people who were leasing the whole brickyard. They were storing crystal glass and ornaments in all the sheds around the old kiln when somebody noticed that the top of the old chimney stack was leaning over and there were a lot of loose bricks on the head; very worrying when you are storing valuable glass below. They had heard about me and my work on local churches and wondered if I could help.

Within the next couple of days I visited the site and what a pleasure it was looking around the old workings; I couldn't understand why I hadn't looked around before. They chimney was square on plan and about 100 feet high, not really that big as chimneys go, and it was in very poor condition. It certainly hadn't been used for many years and of course it hadn't been maintained. The top was leaning badly to the south-east and although it had been banded in several places it certainly was not safe. I spoke to the manager and suggested that we could fell it as there was just enough room between two of the sheds. I thought we could drop it quite safely, as the chimney was leaning in the right direction and they wanted to keep the bricks. Neither of the sheds had any windows or doors on that side, so it seemed like the cheapest and quickest way to solve the problem. But the manager had different views and certainly didn't want us to fell the chimney. He was either worried about his glass or had attended one of the talks I had given locally where I often told a story about felling a chimney that had gone wrong.

It was decided to take the chimney down the hard way but cutting a hole in the base and taking the bricks down the inside of the stack; a much longer job.

A couple of weeks later we had our price accepted and one Sunday I was sitting at home when I thought I would go up to the brick works and ladder the chimney, ready to start on Monday. I had arranged to have the gate left open and as I drove in there was a strange eerie silence and looking around at the sheds, with benches for brick-making. I felt that I could almost hear them working. As I approached the kiln I looked up at the dark chimney and felt a bit sad to think I was going to take it all down to a pile of rubble.

I started to run my ladders up and trying to drive my metal spikes (dogs) into old joints proved to be almost impossible. This chimney was built using lime mortar and it had got so hard it was harder than the bricks (so much for lime mortar being soft). I resorted to drilling and using expanding bolts which also helped by reducing the vibrations. I didn't want the loose bricks at the top falling on me! After an hour or so I had reached the top of the chimney. Looking at the top brickwork this chimney was only standing up by the force of habit. I certainly was not going to be able to put a protective fan around the top of the chimney. This was when I decided to use a crane with a cage on it.

After many problems getting a rather large crane around the very narrow lanes to the site we set up and I went up in the cradle first. I came down with a few bricks, by this time a lot of people had come to watch and it seemed they all wanted the top brick off the chimney. We only used the crane for a couple

of days, taking the top few feet off, then we finished
dismantling by working on the wall.

I haven't been down the hill for many years now but I have
no doubt that it still looks very bare looking at the Downs
(lucky we now have signposts) – a very sad day for the
Nyewood brick yard.

Thinking about dismantling this chimney stack makes my
mind wander and I start thinking about the loss of so much of
our country's heritage – other chimneys and vernacular
buildings etc. that we have dismantled over the years. However,
because of our techniques and the lack of greed I also think we
have saved a few!

It is often the case that when asked to repair or reshingle a
church spire several people on the parochial church council are
of the opinion that they could have the spire removed and a flat
roof added for about the same money as repairing it, thereby
saving future generations the cost of maintaining it. Very true,
but it means future generations and future future generations
will not have the opportunity to see what original buildings
looked like. Once gone, gone forever.

Chapter Eight

The Middle East

I was by then starting to get enquiries and work on my own account. It seems there is nothing better than word of mouth. One of those early jobs was a metal chimney a firm liked to have painted with black bitumen every year, a very dirty job. To get to this chimney you had to climb over very fragile asbestos roofs. The factory staff were very worried about our safety, as a few years earlier a man making his way over these roofs to get to the chimney had fallen through and killed himself. We erected timber catwalks across the roofs to the chimney, which seemed to satisfy them. They asked us to paint the chimney on a regular basis and also asked if we would be interested in doing other work for them.

They were a middle-sized company that manufactured military equipment which they sent around the world. One of their products were large domes which the military used to train gunners. They were sixty feet in diameter, each dome a perfect half sphere standing on a five foot wall. A small hole in the top was ready for ventilators to be fitted when the dome was complete. The firm used to manufacture the components and erect the dome on their premises where it would be checked and if everything was in order, dismantled, packed into crates and sent to various regimes around the world.

We were working on their chimney one time and they had just erected a dome for inspection. They got a message from the Israeli military saying that the covering on one of their earlier domes had failed and could they supply a covering that was more suitable for the Middle Eastern climate. The company researched a covering called Uniroof, a white plastic type covering with an asbestos backing that they thought would be right for these domes, but there was a problem. When the domes had originally been built in Israel, the erectors were able to stand on the sections and with the help of scaffolding, fix the covering, but to re-cover the domes they would require large amounts of scaffolding. Could I perhaps help them?

I designed a rig that would enable them to use bosun's chairs to recover the domes. The fact they had just erected a dome on the premises was ideal, as I could demonstrate my design and train two of their employees to use the equipment. The idea was to erect a mast, triangular on plan, from the floor in the centre of the dome and out through the ventilation opening, then to extend it fifteen feet above the dome with fifteen feet jibs forming a Scotch derrick. From these jibs we could hang bosun's chairs and by lowering and lifting the jibs gain comfortable chair access to all areas of the dome.

Together with one of my men I tried this out on the dome at the company's premises. It worked extremely well, until their men tried to use it. They were not at all happy in the chairs, but with the prospect of a free trip to Israel they said they could do the job.

We sold them the derrick, which was constructed from

alloy scaffold tubes and fittings. They crated it and sent it by air to Israel. Then two men and a rep from the roofing company also went to Israel and that was it as far as we were concerned. A month or so later, we were just finishing a job in London when we had a phone call from the dome manufacturers saying that their men could not do the job from bosun's chairs. They had spent the previous three weeks basically doing nothing and the Israelis were not happy. They asked if we could send a couple of our men out to help.

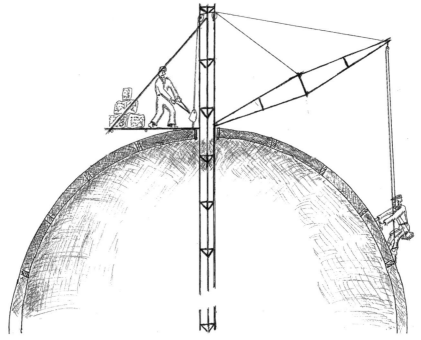

I was not that keen, as I had watched their men trying our equipment in their yard. I told them that I would be prepared to go out there with one of our men provided that I had complete control. They agreed and gave me a letter to that effect to show their men. They agreed to arrange all the tickets and to notify the authorities in Israel.

There were a couple of problems that caused delays, one being that we needed second passports as at that time travel to many countries was unwise with an Israeli stamp in your passport, and we needed inoculations, but a week or so later we were on our way. We arrived in the evening and were met at the airport by one of the company's men in a hire car that had been provided to the firm for the duration of the job. By the time we reached our hotel in Haifa it was around ten o'clock Israeli time. Despite the late hour, I called a meeting in the bar hoping to find out why the job had gone sour.

They had got a couple of Israeli soldiers to erect the derrick for them, as they weren't able to climb the dome. They had tried to use the bosun's chairs and felt they were unsafe. So they'd spent the following couple of weeks sightseeing. They had visited all the religious sites and places of interest, all using the company's hire car while they were on expenses. I decided to send the rep from the roofing company and one other man home on the first available plane, keeping my man and one other with me. I ordered breakfast for five-thirty in the morning and went to bed.

The next day we arrived on site at the Haifa naval base at six thirty, which is not early for that part of the world. After getting clearance to enter the base we drove down to the water's edge, where the dome was situated. The military had stripped the old roof covering off themselves and had erected the derrick. Everything was ready for the new cover, but nothing had been done at all. The Israeli military personnel were certainly not impressed by the British workman.

We started work immediately. The one man we had kept on was a good worker and my mate was used to working out of bosun's chairs. We made good progress from the start and within a week we were just about ready to start dismantling the rigging. At that point a high-ranking officer turned up and asked if we would have a look at another dome when we had finished, this time on an air force base near Hertzliya, around seven kilometres from Tel Aviv.

On arriving at the base, and after convincing the security on the gate that we were not terrorists, they escorted us to the dome. I could hardly believe my eyes. It was smaller than the dome at Haifa and we had been told that it needed re-covering. What they hadn't told us was that one side was almost completely destroyed. A month earlier they had some new recruits in hand-grenade warfare, using live ammunition. One recruit had panicked, pulled the pin and thrown a grenade in the wrong direction, towards the dome. Luckily no one had been hurt, just the dome. I agreed that we could repair it and if they would contact the company in England we could get to the job as soon as we'd finished the first dome in Haifa.

The company certainly got a move on, as they had a new covering made and flown out in just a week. We must have impressed the Israelis, too, as they offered us work in many other parts of their country. It was during our work on the second dome that the Yom Kippur war broke out. Maybe I had offended some of their neighbours.

While we were working repairing the small dome at Hertzliya, we had just had lunch with the captain who was looking after us while we were on the air base, together with his wife and family. I remember it well because it was on Shabbat (their Sabbath) and the lunch consisted of a slow-cooked casserole where the best portion was the one that had the egg. This egg is placed in the casserole raw complete with shell and slowly cooked during the time that religious Jews are forbidden to turn a light on or off. As a foreign visitor I was given the privilege of having this portion. I kept thinking of sheep's eyes and didn't like the idea of eating this egg, but my host Captain Shenhav insisted that he would be offended and insulted if I didn't eat it all.

After lunch we sat and talked for a couple of hours and somehow the subject got round to circumcision. He explained how young boys were all circumcised well before they had their bar mitzvah, but he also told us that the Arabs who lived alongside them waited until the boys were fourteen before they were circumcised and that they used an axe to do it. I didn't really believe him. I thought he was making small talk. No pun intended.

After we finished our lunch and our discussion on religious procedures, my mate and I didn't feel like going back to work. We decided to go for a walk to shake the egg (or sheep's eye) down. It is generally forbidden for civilians to walk around the base unaccompanied, but we were wearing army shirts and trousers and it was Shabbat, so we felt that nobody would notice. Although this is an air force base there were no aeroplanes that wc could see and we assumed that the hangars were underground. I had picked up the captain's lightweight jacket and cap, and was wearing both as we strolled around the base. We even got a couple of very sloppy salutes as we passed a couple of officers of a much lower rank.

We approached the lower end of the parade ground where there was a very long line of Russian lorries, all in military attire and looking very smart and lined up beautifully. We found out much later that these lorries had been left in the Sinai desert, abandoned by a retreating Arab army. It seems that they had been built for the Soviet army to work in Siberia and had overheated in the desert heat. We were told that the Israeli army had designed a new cooling system and they now worked perfectly.

At the far end of this line of lorries, half hidden by some bushes, was a WW-II Patton tank looking a little sorry for itself. My mate, who had never been to Israel before, wanted to take some photos for his album. We both knew this was forbidden, but I had a small camera in my pocket for taking pictures outside the base and on the beach. I agreed and took several photos of him posing against the lorries and the old Patton tank.

I have always been interested in tanks and armoured

vehicles and wanted to see inside this tank. I climbed up and found the hatch on the turret open, so I climbed in. God it was hot in there but I wriggled down onto the driver's seat, which was just a canvas seat like a small deck chair. There was very little room, with thick steel all round you. There were little hooks with strings which hooked onto the driver's helmet to stop his head banging against the side of the driving compartment, all very claustrophobic and I don't know how anyone could stay in there for long with other soldiers and the engine running.

I had only been in there for five minutes when my mate, who had been peeping through a little hatch and taking photos, said, "I would get out of there as quickly as you can."

I thought there must have been someone coming, but I was just starting to enjoy myself. I was driving a WW-II Patton tank into battle, in my mind anyway. I had just blown three enemy tanks off the face of the earth and was lining up on another when my mate, sounding much more urgent this time, said: "Get out of there, quickly!" This time he was shouting to me through the small opening the driver looks through. So I climbed out, with great difficulty, banging my head and knees as I did so.

I jumped down to the ground where my mate was waiting and asked: "What's the problem?" He told me to look through the little opening, where – once my eyes had got used to the light – I could see, under the little driver's seat, a huge lizard-type creature. It was about two foot six inches long and really ugly. If I had looked under the seat when I was sitting there I think I would have tested the armour plating of that tank, but my mate got his photos anyway and no harm was done.

A few days after, me and my mate were staying in Hertzliya in a very nice, very Israeli hotel and the other fellow who worked for the contractors had never even heard of the Jewish New Year and thought everyone celebrated New Year in January. I had never celebrated Rosh Hashanah in Israel during peacetime. So we invited the other fellow to our hotel for the main meal, a wonderful time to spend in Israel. This was four-day holiday, where the religious Jews spend a lot of time in prayer at the shul, but the evening meal is quite something to watch or to be part of. Our colleague from Haifa arrived with an interpreter, who was a beautiful Israeli girl which made my mate very jealous and I think he wished he had stayed in Haifa instead of coming with me, but a great evening was had by all. My mate and the other fellow went on to a disco. I had a drink with a couple of soldiers and went to bed. A wonderful evening in a wonderful country.

After the festival of Rosh Hashanah, our mate went back to Haifa to complete the dome there. Me and my mate carried on at Hertzliya repairing the smaller dome. It was extremely hot; even the local soldiers were wilting under the heat. They were surprised just how hot it was, very unusual at that time of the year. Our work was very physical and I was feeling the heat more than most. I was suffering from thirst and completely forgot my army training about drinking. I was drinking gallons of red grape juice, ridiculous when you think back on it. I became really quite sick with diarrhoea and exhaustion. The sergeant who was looking after us decided I was too sick to work. As we were visitors in his country he felt responsible for us and called for a medic, who promptly sent us back to our hotel.

There were a lot of tourists staying in this hotel and they must have wondered who we were, when they brought us back to the hotel in massive army vehicles with gun-carrying soldiers and escorted us up to our rooms, followed by a medical team. They really do look after foreign visitors to their land.

Chapter Nine

Traditional Steeplejacking

Soon after returning from Israel, and after catching up on our regular contract work on churches and cathedrals, we were asked to carry out an inspection of the spire at Chichester Cathedral. At that time there were major works being carried out on the main body of the cathedral. There was scaffolding in place up to the tower parapet. The plan was to ladder the spire, to ascertain what repairs were necessary, before any more scaffolding was erected at that level. Usually, I like to fix my own ladders but on this occasion my mate Bob (who soon went with his brothers to work on their own, very successfully I believe) fixed the ladders and I carried them for him.

After the inspection, and after our report had been digested, the committee decided that they would still scaffold the complete spire, even though there was only a small amount of work needed. That was not merely my opinion; one of the architects had also climbed up our ladders. They got prices from several scaffolding companies to design and erect a full scaffold from the parapet to the apex – enormous amounts of money. I could not see how this expense could be justified and as I always champion the church, I felt that I had to do something. I looked up the address of the treasurer and went to see him.

He lived in a very large house and as I approached I certainly had second thoughts about whether I was doing the right thing, but I knocked on the door and was greeted friendlily. I explained that there was little work to be done on the spire and that the cost of the actual work would be similar whether the spire was scaffolded up or accessed by steeplejack methods, so why spend tens of thousands putting up a lot of unnecessary scaffolding. He agreed and a week or so later I was asked to attend a meeting where they offered me the job.

This was an interesting job as it brought to light a couple of fascinating features. It had always been assumed the weather vane on top of the spire was the original and the one displayed in the cathedral had been on top of the bell tower during the time the spire was down following its collapse in 1861. In fact it was the other way round and the weather vane in the cathedral is the one that adorned the original spire.

The job consisted of bringing down the weather vane for the Cathedral Works Organisation to gild, some general pointing and applying a shelter coat of hydraulic lime to the top fifty feet of the spire. I was concerned that the shelter coat would stand out like a sore thumb, but they insisted. So we went ahead, but to cover my own backside I got their men to mix up the shelter coat.

As soon as we had finished the work, the architect and I climbed the spire so that he could inspect the work and assure everyone who thought it should have been scaffolded that it was a job well done. This was the start of a good association with Cathedral Works and the architects, who both gave us work over the following twenty to thirty years.

One job they gave us was on a very large Victorian church in London. This was a red brick and Bath stone building with a very tall tower topped with a large slate-covered broach spire. It had a large nave with a massive slate roof; the rafter length must have been at least fifty feet. We often use the term "church pitch". This roof certainly lived up to that name.

We were asked to erect a platform inside, up near the collars, to give others access to fit some electrical equipment. The platform was completely boarded out and all the nave lights had been pulled up, so when anyone walked into the nave there were only a few small lights fixed near the pews. If you looked up it was completely dark, with the exception of a small opening, about three feet square, through which we hauled up equipment for ourselves and the electricians.

We were putting the finishing touches to our platform, nailing down loose boards and so on, and were talking and laughing when the priest appeared on the platform. He told us that they were about to have a service and asked if we would be quiet during their service. He suggested we have a cup of tea and a smoke, which was allowed back then. We did, and soon the small area above the boarded platform was like a proper London smog, a real pea-souper.

I had never seen a Catholic service, so I crawled along the boards to the small opening and peered down. Soon after, a little old lady came scuttling up the aisle and sat down on a pew below me. She leaned forward to pray. It is amazing how right up in the roof you can hear every word being spoken below. This little old lady was muttering her prayers when she started to speak louder. Perhaps she thought the Lord could hear her better if she shouted. She was saying, "Oh Lord, I've got very serious problems and I don't know what to do". She went on to describe her problems but I'm not going to share that with you. She just kept on saying, "Lord, please just give me a sign!" and repeating that all she needed was a sign. When she looked up shortly after, she saw the little opening, all lit up and misty with smoke, and a bearded face looking down at her.

I spoke to the priest afterwards and he told me that he had been at the rear of the church during the service, as his colleague was officiating, and the little old lady had come flying down the aisle after the service, clutching her coat about herself and saying in a loud voice "I only asked for a sign; you didn't have to come yourself."

The same architects asked us to go to St Mary le Strand. This is a typical London church, all weathered Portland stone, situated just where the Strand divides. It seemed that somebody had found a lump of stone in the middle of the road next to the church that appeared to match the weathered stone on the church. That made sense, as the church was much older than the building opposite. The architects were worried there might be more about to fall, so we were asked to climb the tower to find where this piece of stone had come from.

A surveyor from Westminster City Council was involved. We would need to rope off part of the road while we worked, so I asked him if he had the authority to order this. He looked a little upset that I had any doubts about his importance, assuring me: "If I want to I can close the whole Strand!" I was glad it wasn't necessary to do that, as I could imagine the chaos it would have caused at rush hour. I explained that given our methods of access it would be fine to just rope off a small area at a time. This seemed to satisfy him and we started work.

We ranged over the complete tower and spire, found where the stone had fallen from and also identified several more cracks and a lot of spalling stone from the cramps, which were not very deep. It was decided to scaffold the top part of the tower and get stonemasons to carry out these repairs, which they did at a cost of some £150,000. Before the scaffolding was removed the architects carried out a final inspection and decided that the spire was unsafe. A few months later, with new architects, they scaffolded the whole tower and spire again, dismantled the spire and rebuilt it, using as much of the original stone as possible but renewing all the cramps with stainless steel. We were only involved with gilding the weather vane and clock dial.

I have always admired the way smartly dressed women with fashionable short skirts get in and out of cars so elegantly without showing the world their underwear. On this church I met the absolute master, or rather mistress, of this art.

Towards the end of the rebuild, when there was scaffolding up to within thirty feet of the weather vane, St Mary le Strand became the official church of the Women's Royal Naval Service and the Association of Wrens. On the day of dedication, a ceremony was held in the church with the Commandant and many other Wrens all looking very smart in their uniforms.

After the ceremony, the Commandant decided that she wanted to climb the scaffold to the top deck where the dedication was to take place. She climbed the scaffolding surrounded by architects and male officers who were really fussing around the poor woman.

When she reached the top platform and looked up at the gleaming weather vane, she decided that she wanted to climb up our ladders to have her photo taken beside the weather vane.

I already had safety lines fitted to the spire, but as she was wearing a tight smart skirt we couldn't fit a safety harness between her legs, a belt would have to suffice. She insisted on "going aloft". I was a little concerned as there were about 15 fifteen men on the scaffold. She asked me, as the steeplejack on site, to accompany her. Well, I followed as closely as decently possible, trying to obscure the view from below. I needn't have worried. She climbed the ladders right up to the weather vane and posed for the cameras with such elegance and style that she was the mistress of poise.

It is always good when one job finishes and another is ready to start, as you can move equipment between sites as it comes down. So as this job started to close we moved our equipment to St Stephen Walbrook in the City of London, where a large restoration project was in hand. Our part in this was going to be to repair and gild the weather vane as well as to repair the large lead-covered timber ball which topped the lantern on the copper dome above the nave. The ball is two feet in diameter and carved from a single piece of timber. I believe it is sweet chestnut, which is very unusual as most chestnut is coppiced when young. I often wonder what happened to the rest of the tree.

The rather shallow dome is interesting, as it is widely said that Sir Christopher Wren built this dome to help him design the dome of St Paul's Cathedral. I don't see how that can be true, as this dome is a simple self-supporting structure whereas the outside dome of St Paul's is supported on a brick cone. But there's always a story, not necessarily accurate but often interesting.

At this time we always seemed to be working in London. Before we had finished at St Stephen Walbrook we were asked to do an inspection of All Souls near Oxford Circus. This is a very interesting building with a strange spire that is sometimes called the candle snuffer because there is no finial or weather vane, just a large bronze cone. There is an amusing story that soon after it was built a magazine published a cartoon of the architect, who designed the spire, being lowered bottom first onto this sharp pointed cone.

We were riding down over the parapet and on reaching the Corinthian columns were surprised that when we tapped the capitals instead of the familiar dull noise there was a ringing, like a bell. This was my introduction to Coade stone. This is a manufactured stone, made to a formula developed by Eleanor Coade in the nineteenth century. It is an extremely durable substitute for natural stone that has stood the test of time. One final example of this stone's use is the lion that used to adorn the Red Lion Brewery and now stands proudly on the south side of Westminster Bridge. There are many other places where Coade stone has been used, from grand buildings to garden ornaments. There are also many well-known tombs in churchyards around the country and an awful lot of small crosses and features that are not so easily recognised.

It was while we were repairing several of the smaller features in a churchyard near Windsor that we were asked to quote a price for reshingling the spire at Old Windsor. One afternoon, I went to measure the spire. It was a small broach spire, down near the river. I carefully measured it, using an optical measure, and sent my estimate to the architects. In due course we were given the order and told that they would like us to start as soon as possible. I managed to put off another job that we had planned to start and a week or so later we turned up with our equipment and started to ladder the tower.

After a while an elderly gentleman who was walking past with his dog stopped and asked us what we were doing to his church. I explained that we were rigging ready for re-shingling. He seemed a little put out and explained that, as he was churchwarden, he was rather surprised no one had told him that we were starting or indeed even let him know that they were having the spire re-shingled. Just to be sure, I asked him if this was Old Windsor. He looked puzzled and replied that no, this was Cullvers and that Old Windsor was about three miles away. The dimensions were similar and I had no idea, but by now it was very clear that we had started on the wrong church. We apologised, removed our ladders, loaded up our equipment and drove off towards the right church. We were very lucky that both churches were very similar in size, so no harm had been done.

Chapter Ten

Back to Cornwall

A friend who ran a scaffolding company in Cornwall rang me and asked if I could help him with a job on an old mine chimney that would have to come down to make way for development. Several other companies had quoted for the job, but he hoped I would come up with something that would give his firm the edge. So I drove down to Cornwall.

The job was very near Penryn, a typical Cornish chimney. The base was constructed from Cornish granite, very irregular stones with large lime mortar joints. Most of this mortar was falling out, leaving large deep openings – very unstable. It was circular on plan and built of stone for the first fifty feet, then it changed to hard red brick with cement-rich mortar joints which were extremely hard. At the top was a small corbelled head, giving the chimney a total height of around eighty feet. There were some industrial buildings around the base that were to be kept. These were quite fragile buildings and wouldn't have stood much scaffolding bearing on them.

I suggested that the best and cheapest method would be to ladder the chimney and work on the wall, knock a hole in the base and knock it down a course at a time. My friend agreed and priced it accordingly. Within a week he was asking us to go ahead as soon as we could. Very soon were heading back to Cornwall, back to the same digs ready to start work. I had reckoned with about a week to do the job, so we couldn't afford to hang about.

The next morning we got the ladders up with some difficulty. It was hard to get a good fixing on the lower part, because the joints were too wide, and on the upper section the joints were too hard. This was before the days of battery-operated hammer drills. But we managed with blood, sweat and tears.

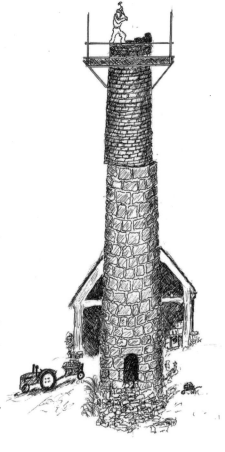

The top couple of courses came off quite easily, but then it got really hard. The bricks were breaking up before the joints would give, but with a fourteen pound sledge hammer it soon started to come apart. We carried on with the sledge hammer all afternoon. As we were climbing down, I noticed that where the brickwork met the stonework it didn't line up. I hadn't noticed that as we'd laddered, but thought it was a case of the builders not having got it right.

Next morning, back up early with the big hammer. Coming down for tea I noticed that the misalignment looked worse but as I hadn't measured it, I wasn't sure. On the way back up I did measure it, then forgot all about it until we came down again. I measured the step again and it had definitely moved. This meant that as we were working away at the top the chimney had been swaying and slowly walking towards Truro.

After we realised what was happening we slowed down with the hammer and kept an eye on the step. Even though we had to go a lot more slowly we still got the chimney down in the time allotted, so it was a good job and a good earner for all concerned.

We were just about to leave Cornwall, without bellies full of pasties, when another builder asked the scaffolding company if we would look at a job for them while we were there. This was a tower on the harbour wall at Porthleven, a small fishing village that we knew from before when we had worked on the cliffs above the fisheries.

There was a granite tower with a small lead turret right out at the end of the harbour. We were asked to provide access to the parapet, as all the floors and stairs inside the tower had rotted away. The day we arrived it was blowing a gale. We started to unload our ladders, but the wind was so strong that it was difficult to carry them even at ground level. So we stacked them in a small yard at the back, called it a day and went to sample the local beer.

The next day the weather was better. We started putting up our ladders. I was fixing and my mate carrying. It was a very hard and laborious job, because of the very narrow joints and hard granite, but by teatime I had reached the corbels just below the parapet. By reaching up and holding onto the coping stones I could look through the crenelations and into the gutter, which as expected was full of muck. With no human access up here for many years the local birds had taken over. I was just about to go down for tea when out of the corner of my eye I saw a movement. I turned and in the opposite corner, standing on the parapet, was an enormous bird. It was truly massive. I think it was an albatross, with a huge hooked beak and a great big black eye looking straight at me. I don't remember exactly, but I think I said "Hello Birdy". It kept looking straight at me. I don't think it liked being called Birdy. For what seemed an age we just looked at each other, then it started to come towards me. It didn't walk, it sort of jumped and hopped, then jumped and hopped again, with its huge beak wide open and making an awful noise. I quickly scrambled down the ladders. It was definitely time for a tea break and I needed to think.

As we were sitting drinking tea, an old sea dog appeared and asked us what we were doing.

I told him we were going to clean out the parapet gutters and fix the weather vane and finial, but that there was a great big ugly albatross that thought it owned the place and also obviously didn't like me.

He laughed and said, "So you've met our seagull then?"

If it was a seagull then it was a very, very big one. I am still sure it was an albatross, a very bad tempered albatross. He told us that a pair of seagulls had been nesting up on the tower for years and as their young ones had flown they wouldn't attack us. He said that the bird was probably fascinated by our funny accents. (He could talk, my handsome.) He also said that if we met him at lunchtime at the Ship public house, where he was about to head, he could tell us many a thing about the tower and the seagulls. As the bird had flown away, after our tea break we carried on fixing the ladders and rigging our ropes and equipment ready to start lowering the muck. But I thought it might be good PR to meet the old chap at lunchtime.

This was a very friendly pub and the locals were chatty and interested in what we were doing. The old man told us that in the old days when the fishing boats came in at night there was a light fixed to the finial which, when lined up with a light up in the harbour, would guide them in safely through the narrow opening of the harbour entrance. He told us that it had not been used for many years, as with modern navigation systems it wasn't necessary. But a few of the older boats would find it useful, so we should make sure that we got it right. I told him that we would certainly do our best and when we got the weathervane and finial down on the ground he would be welcome to come and inspect it.

We didn't speak to him again for a while, as we were working on the top of the tower, but we waved to him as he walked by most mornings. A couple of weeks later, when we were refitting the finial, he called us down and said that we'd got the weathervane the wrong way round and that North was a few degrees further left. I explained that on this particular finial there was a locating peg, so it was impossible to get it wrong, and if he wanted to get have his light in the right place that's where it would have to stay. He went away, muttering about "bloody upcountry people who think they know everything", but in the end he thought we'd done "a proper job, my handsomes."

It was during this job that I had to go to the courthouse at Penryn. In those days commercial vehicles were restricted to 40 mph and as we mostly travelled to and from Cornwall at night we sometimes exceeded that speed and were stopped once or twice by the police. On this occasion I was going to

pay my fine and hopefully keep my licence. After paying my
dues I thought I would get some lunch and remembered that,
when we were working in Penryn before, someone had
recommended a café to us that was known for its pasties. So I
decided to try it out. I walked into the café and a very large
Cornish lady looked at me from behind the counter and bared
her teeth. I wasn't sure if it was a smile or a snarl. She spoke
just one word, "Yes?" So I showed her my teeth and said
"Pasty and chips, please."

"Oh no, we don't do chips, 'tis only pasties here my lover."
I thought that strange, but told her it was fine and I'd just have
a 'tis only pasty then.

She picked up a plate and dropped it noisily onto the
counter. She was a large woman with what looked like a bunch
of bananas on the end of each arm. She turned and picked up a
huge pasty, which hung over the sides of the plate. It looked
like a young dinosaur. It was massive. No wonder they don't
serve chips with them. Eat one of those and you can't move.

St. Peter's and Holy Cross, Wherwell, Hampshire

The parochial church council arranged a barbeque when this restored cockerel was returned to the top of the church — I was allowed extra sausages!

The 'Three Hacketts'

When I used to give talks to historical societies and the like, I used these pictures to make a point. For some reason, whenever I went to a new job one of the first things the people (the churchwarden, the vicar and most of the parishioners) would say to me is "you don't look like a steeplejack". They had obviously been watching Fred Dibnah on TV. I would explain that I had the flat cap and was working on the large beer belly, but they were not convinced. So I would tell them this story about the Hacketts.

The Hacketts were a family of steeplejacks who had lived and worked some 50 to 60 years ago. They were thought by most people in the trade to be the best and nobody doubted them. I explained that I was very lucky to have three photographs of them which I used to display on my laptop projector.

There was "Old pipe smoking Hackett" who was standing on a deck some two hundred feet above Dorking.

Then there was "Old Humpty Back Hackett" photographed on a deck on the same church, well wrapped up against the wind because of his hunchback.

The third Hackett is known as "Robin Hood Hackett" and if you look closely you can still see the arrow that pierced his balaclava.

When you are gilding a clock dial from a bosun's chair, people often ask where you keep the brushes — well now you know.

The fourth picture is of me with the Guildford cathedral angel. If you look closely you will have to agree that I do, or did, look like a steeplejack.

St. John's, Higham, Kent

This beautiful Bath stone spire was in a very poor condition when we arrived. The whole top was loose and swaying in the wind. All the joints had gone and the weather vane and finial were in a sorry state. So we had to rebuild the top ten feet or so.

Not wanting to travel too far we looked for somewhere to park our caravan. The obvious and only place was a small yard very close to the church. After some very hard negotiations with the owner we were allowed to park there. What we hadn't been told was that he kept a very large goat as a guard. So getting out the caravan it was a case of opening the door and running for the gate! We even tried to bribe the goat with food but he still didn't like us staying there.

Cathedral Church of St Michael and St George, Aldershot, Hampshire

We extended the weathervane to make this the tallest garrison church; anything to please the vicar.

High level gardening

Some time ago we were asked to look at some old lime kilns at Betchworth, Dorking which had been laying idle for many years. We were asked to provide access to allow a firm of surveyors to examine them. This was all straightforward stuff and we didn't have too many problems.

But there was one kiln on the site that was covered with amazing growth of ivy. This kiln was brand new and it had never been used. It was probably over a hundred years old and under the ivy was a brand spanking new brick lime kiln exactly as it was built. It seemed somebody had invented cement and the sales of lime had fallen. The Surrey Wildlife Trust had decided to

make this a bat habitat, but to do this they needed the ivy taken off.

We were asked to supply access up to the top of the kiln, put a platform around the top, strip off all the ivy and assist the team of surveyors to examine the tower inside and out.

We put a rig on the top of the kiln to lower the surveyors down inside and while they worked on the inside we could start stripping the ivy from the outside.

We had rigged bosun's chairs from the scaffold around the top and had just started working when a van pulled up and two wood choppers (tree surgeons) got out. I went down to see them and I realised that I knew one of them. He asked if they could come up onto the kiln and have a look around and any chance they could have a go in a bosun's chair. I agreed but insisted that on their chairs there would be an extra safety line as it was their first time. On the pictures you will see that the two men in the middle have an extra safety line, are wearing different helmets and are thoroughly enjoying themselves.

Lancing College, West Sussex

Other work

Sompting Abbotts School, West Sussex

A climbing scaffold was used for cladding this chimney in Avonmouth.

St Peter & St Paul, Ewhurst, Surrey

One very large corbel fell through the Horsham stone roof and this scaffold was put up to stop any others falling through the roof. It stayed for three years while they raised the money for repairs.

I believe this church was unique as all the shingles to the spire were arrow-heads and it is the only time I have seen a complete spire in oak with decorated shingles.

Cathedral Church of the Holy Spirit, Guildford, Surrey

Laddering up inside the cathedral to inspect the top of the arch.

This angel weather vane, because of its position on top of a lofty tower on top of a very large hill, is very prone to extreme weather conditions.

Never more so than in October 1987 when there was probably the worst storm in living memory which took clay tiles up from the roofs of houses down below in The Oval. If you look at the front of Gabriel's robe you will see the dents where these tiles landed.

Of course there has been a lot of debris blown up onto the tower roof over the years but all much lighter. But some years ago, during a heavy storm, a swan was flying around the cathedral admiring the wonderful view that we all love from the height of the tower when a sudden gust of wind blew one of them into the Angel and the swan died; very sad.

Photo Copyright Mirrorpix.

St. Nicholas, Compton, Surrey

While topping out this spire somebody from the church came up with some ancient tradition that you put a branch of a tree up with the weathervane to ward off evil spirits. The branch fell down but the spire still stands (at the moment).

St. Martin's, Dorking, Surrey

The author and a newspaper man climbing up to take pictures.

St. Michael &
All Angels,
Mickleham, Surrey

Erecting a flying deck before removing the weather cock for repairs and re-gilding.

Shingling the spire from bosuns chairs.

This is a good example of a shingled spire on top of a Norman tower.

The Old Brickworks, Nyewood, West Sussex

This local chimney was 92ft high, 9ft across the bottom and 7ft across the top and. It was built in 1900 and last used in 1966 before being taken down in March 1984.

Holy Trinity, Hawley, Hampshire

The site of the only fall we had in all those years. The bride had to wait, the man survived with only minor injuries.

The Donkey

Whenever you ladder a church spire anywhere in the country and you get down again for a cup of tea or whatever, there is always someone who comes out and asks: "Are you taking the weather vane down?" Because they remember it coming down the last time and they remember that it took three or four men to lift it. It was so big that they could not fit it into the vicar's shed for safety so they put it in a garage nearby. They always remember that it was as big

as a donkey, sometimes it's as big as a horse but whatever they compare it to, it was always very large.

In my experience most weathervanes are generally disproportionately small. So when we get a large cockerel or flag weather vane in our yard to repair or gild it always gets known as 'the donkey'.

On one very large church in Brentwood, Essex the weather cockerel was large — probably the largest cockerel that I have gilded. It was of course, christened 'the donkey'. We bought it down to gild and even though it was a large cockerel the people watching were disappointed with its size.

Some weeks later when we were hoisting the finial back to the top of the spire, several of them commented on the size and weight of the donkey. These photos show the size and the problem of putting it back to its lofty perch – 180ft up.

One of our men had a similar argument in his local pub about the weathervane from St. Martin's, Dorking.

Again, the locals had seen it down many years before and remembered first how big it was and our chap could not convince them. So he borrowed the cockered and stood it on the bar in the pub, proving that it was their memory playing tricks.

St. Peter & St. Paul,
Peasmarsh, East Sussex

During the re-shingling of this complete spire we rebuilt the top, recovered the boss and apex with sandcast lead and added a lantern fixing to the finial.

St. James' Parish Church,
Weybridge, Surrey

An apprentice gilder working on the clock face.

Victoria Tower,
Palace of Westminster,
London

If I look thoughtful in this picture it is only because I am out of baccy and nobody here smokes a pipe.

If you look up at the pinnacles you will see our access scaffolds, not very clear in this picture.

But in this picture there is a much better and closer view of the scaffolding. This was erected before we were asked to assist and train the other steeplejacks working on site.

It seemed that the other jacks were having problems with the gilding, the site engineer was very strict and knowledgeable about gilding.

There are four cast iron crowns on the tower and the weather was very cold (February) so the metal was cold and damp. The mist in the morning was also very slow to lift, not giving a long day. Also, for some reason they had decided to gild the inside of the crowns. There were many layers of old paint that needed to be chipped off if a good finish was to be achieved.

But they had painted and then gilded the whole inside of the crowns so when inspected very closely the appearance was not what was expected, that's when we were asked to help.

The first thing I did was to get permission to have a gas blow lamp on site, no mean feat with their fire regulations. We stripped off the paint back to bare metal, primed and painted the whole crown. When dry we heated up the metal, wrapped a plastic sheet around each crown and started gilding. We gilded only what could be seen from below saving a lot of time and gold leaf with the slightly warm metal the size hardened at a steady and constant rate; a very enjoyable job.

While working on these crowns I looked down one of the large stone spires which I was told was just a ventilator. At the apex there is a bronze finial which is bent over. I was told how during the war, when a barrage balloon broke away from its moorings and the cable got twisted around the finial and bent it the RAF shot it down. Could be true.

A steeplejack's view from Victoria Tower.

Shalford Chimney, Guildford, Surrey

There used to be a tall brick chimney just behind The Parrot public house in Shalford. The factory had closed its doors and been sold for redevelopment but the chimney was still standing proud overlooking the river.

The local paper I believe, had arranged a competition and the winner was to push the plunger to blow the whole thing down.

A couple of weeks before the event somebody climbed up the chimney and hung a dummy from the lightning conductor so from the ground it looked like somebody had hung themselves.

Some lady walking her dog called the police who quickly arrived with binoculars and soon realised that it was a dummy. They could find no way up so it was decided to leave it there until the demolition of the chimney.

The chimney was eventually blown down. When the police rescued the dummy it was wearing a pair of my overalls, sign-written on the back, stuffed and with a pipe in its mouth. After the police visited me they decided that it must have been one of my employees with a grudge.

St Mary's, Battersea, London

To my knowledge this is the only copper spire where the bulk of the recovering was carried out from bosun chairs — great savings for the church.

St. Andrew & St. Mary the Virgin, Fletching, West Sussex

This job was used as a training program for several roofers; one of the trainees learning to abscil.

This is the remains of the old lookout. On high days and holidays flags would have been flown from here. Very rarely used by modern steeplejacks. A very hard climb up inside; much easier to ladder up outside.

Spire Tops

St. Peter & St. Paul,

Peasmarsh, East Sussex

Rebuilt top, repaired boss, sand cast lead, lantern fixing.

An apex before the lead covering was added showing the holes for trickle ventilation.

All Saints Church,

Farringdon, Hampshire

Local blacksmith's lantern fixing, rebuilt top, octagonal boss with scoop ventilators.

All our lead was code 7 sand cast.

Central Church, Torquay, Devon

I got a phone call: "We think we have a hole in our spire, its leaking. Can you have a look?"

This picture shows that I checked right up to the very top and still couldn't find the leak.

St. Mary & St. Gabriel, South Harting, West Sussex

Local children watching the cockerel going up with great interest. The front two look like budding steeplejacks.

St. George's, Trotton, West Sussex

This church has many visitors because of its ancient brasses and wall paintings.

When we were asked to reshingle the spire of St. George's at Trotton they insisted that it should be done in the traditional way, or as near as possible to the method that the original church builders would have used.

At the time when we looked at the church it was covered with hand cleft oak shingles but these were not original as the spire had been recovered some sixty years before.

We checked the boarding and found that some very old boarding had survived, very thin oak pit sawn boards with the remains of old chestnut pegs; unusual as we would have expected cleft oak pegs.

Knowing the area well and the amount of chestnut coppice growing and still being coppiced we decided to recover with hand cleft and drawn knifed chestnut shingles.

There was this old woodman coppicing a parcel of land on the hill a few hundred yards away up the hill towards Rogate. Most of what he was cutting was too young for our needs, but towards the top of the hill there was a large patch of about 30 year old straight chestnut which he was willing to sell to us at a reasonable price.

He cut it into six foot lengths for us, then we cut these into one foot lengths and cleft them across the block (not on the quarter as in oak). We set up two shave horses one on the hill and one in the churchyard and the made the first 5,000 shingles.

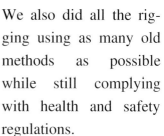

We also did all the rigging using as many old methods as possible while still complying with health and safety regulations.

The job created a lot of interest from artists', photographers and local historical societies.

This very unoriginal weather cockerel was gilded, a handsome spire it looked.

Holy Trinity at Twydall, Gillingham, Kent

When we were asked to do some shingle repairs to a church at Twydall Green, Kent I was expecting a shingled spire. So I was quite surprised when I saw the church.

At first glance it looked like a badly kept bus shelter, the brickwork was very uneven and there were very large areas of shingled roof slope.

But as we climbed these steep roof slopes it was obvious why they had called in steeplejacks.

It might have won an award, but whoever built it didn't think much about maintenance.

We were asked to change some of the glass, which was a real challenge, but by the time we had finished I could really see why this unusual church had won a well-deserved award.

**Wimbledon,
a steeplejack's view**

A great place to watch the tennis!

Mid Wales Hospital, Talgarth (1969)

Part of the job was to remove the old molar brick lining from inside the chimney. This we did from bosun's chairs but there was a void between the lining and the outer brickwork which was full of soot, so it was a very dirty job. There was very little in the way of washing facilities and we couldn't go back to our lodgings in such a filthy state. The only answer was to use a bath that was in the mortuary.

This bath was only there to wash bodies. I thought that if I cleaned it out it would be all right. I was surprised at the amount of finger and toe nails that were in there. It seems that finger and toe nails continue to grow after death. I am not sure that this is true but it is what the mortuary attendant told me (you learn something new every day).

I filled the bath with hot water and the same chap found me some washing-up liquid that I poured in making lovely bubbles. I stripped off and jumped in. I threw all my clothes and boots in as well as I needed them clean to go back to the lodgings.

I had just started to relax and enjoy my bath, doing my washing at the same time, when my mates came in for a laugh. They also reminded me of a stupid remark I had made some time before when on one hot day I had said that could climb the ladder to the top of the chimney naked, walk around the top and nobody would even notice.

Not wanting to back down I climbed out of the bath and across the yard clutching parts of my body for modesty and started to climb the ladders. I hadn't realised just how tender the soles of my feet were. I struggled slowly to the top and was glad to stand on the brickwork which was comfortable by comparison with the ladders. Then the painful climb down and back to finish my bath.

I had just got into my bath when the matron from the hospital came storming in, she was furious, and told me she had watched me climb up and down and it was pathetic. Obviously, she had very good eyesight. I was surprised that if she was so horrified she had watched me climb up and down! I'll bet she had a camera.

This silhouette was taken by the local camera club at dusk for a competition and won.

Weathervanes

St. Paul,
East Molesey, Surrey

St. Mary Le Strand,
London

St. Laurence Church, Catsfield, East Sussex

St. Bartholomew's, Wickham Bishops, Essex

A good example of symmetrical cedar shingling. This photo was used by the shingle supplier as their Christmas card — maybe it was the red overalls and beard?

It was during this time that I heard from one of our men who had stayed behind after we had finished an earlier job, because he had fallen in love with the only girl in the world for him. He had gone looking for work and was offered a job with a scaffolding company. He had told them that he had worked on some very large projects and had experience in all types of rigging. One of the main reasons for them to employ him was his expertise in rigging cradles and suspended platforms. It seemed that there had not been much cradle usage in Cornwall, but with modern building methods there would be a need. At the first opportunity the scaffolding company had bought some cradle equipment and from then on recommended the use of cradles whenever they saw an opportunity.

Sooner rather than later an opportunity appeared in Truro, on a four-storey building. Perhaps not the best shaped building to start rigging cradles on, but our ex-employee told them that it was possible and that if you had experience you could rig cradles on almost any type of building. He drew up a list of all the materials he needed and the scaffolding company delivered everything to the site along with a couple of scaffolders to help him and also to learn.

They rigged the cradle and tried it out. It was a travelling cradle with two lengths of track. One end of the track stuck out past the end of the building by about three feet and the stop had been fixed at the end of the track, not the edge of the building. So when the cradle passed the end of the building onto the unsupported part of the track, one end dropped, leaving the cradle – with two men inside – dangling on a single rope.

Both men managed to hang on, but they were frightened to move in case the whole lot came down.

The fire brigade were called and using their own equipment managed to get the men down safely. The scaffolding company responded very quickly, removing all the cradle gear and scaffolding the building conventionally. The next day the painters turned up, disappointed not to be using cradles.

When our former employee was asked to explain what went wrong, he had replied that he had erected the equipment exactly as we had taught him. Of all the cradles and suspended platforms we have erected over the years, not one has failed. A little knowledge truly can be a dangerous thing.

As I was driving back from the courthouse at Penryn I passed the hospital at Treliske. Always on the lookout for work, I noticed that their chimney stack was looking rather tired and shabby so I called in to see the engineer. This chimney was not very big, about a hundred feet tall, constructed from concrete with steel multi-flue liners. The top ten feet or so was painted black but was starting to peel and needed a little attention. There were threaded bronze sockets all the way up one side as permanent fixings.

Before I finally got to meet the engineer I had to persuade a couple of very prickly Cornish assistants that I was genuine. He told me a story about the chimney and how it was he who had suggested that they build in the permanent fixings to help people like me. He also told me that when they were building the chimney he had fallen out with the foreman about the finished appearance of the concrete. The foreman had told him that he was stupid and to wait until the chimney was completed before criticising his work. The chimney was about halfway to completion at that point, but the engineer was not happy, not prepared to wait and promptly gave the foreman a month's notice. If you look at the chimney from some angles you can see that it is perfectly straight up until the halfway mark, then leans off at a slight angle. Perhaps the engineer should have given the foreman a month's pay in lieu of notice.

The bronze rings that screw into the sockets for permanent fixings had been stolen, so the engineer wouldn't let anyone climb the chimney. Goodbye.

Chapter Eleven

Unexplained Happenings

W e were working on a church in Kent, on a large stone spire. The men had their caravan parked at a public house a couple of miles from the job. It suited them and they had stayed there on several occasions, but I decided to stay in my caravan at the church. Usually there is a car park or field nearby, but in this case there really was nowhere. I asked the vicar if he had any objections to me parking my caravan in the churchyard. He wasn't happy with the idea, but could not think of anywhere else. He said I could park in front of the church for one night and he would think of something.

The next morning he arrived at the church early and had a cup of tea with me as I ate my breakfast. He said that he had rung round everywhere and had no luck but there was a place right down the back of the churchyard under some trees. I could not drive down there and we would have to manhandle the caravan. I told him as soon as the men turned up that's what we would do. He walked with me down to the site, it was right down at the bottom of the graveyard under some yew trees and where he said we could put the caravan there was an old rusty iron cross but no inscription. I had my doubts, but he insisted it was okay and there was nowhere else and he didn't want it seen by the parishioners.

He went home for breakfast just as the men turned up. We then manhandled my caravan down to the agreed site with great difficulty – it was a heavy caravan over rough ground – but eventually got it under the trees and on top of the old grave. I apologised to whoever was down there and extended the pipes that drain from the caravan so no waste water went near the grave.

It was several nights later when I was woken up by something or somebody knocking on the floor of my caravan. If I'd had any hair it would have stood on end, then without thinking I shouted "Come in!" Nobody came in. I looked out of the window. It was a beautiful bright moonlit night. I could not see anything or anybody, so-- back to sleep! I don't know how long I slept but I was suddenly woken by knocking on the floor again. My heart was really thumping in my chest but again without thinking I shouted "Come in!" Nobody came in. "It's no good, I have got to do something", I thought, so I got out of bed and went to the door. I thought I would leap out of the door, turn and face whoever or whatever was under my caravan. I leapt out of the door with a mighty bound, turned to face it – and to my surprise all there was under the caravan were two woolly lambs jumping about, knocking against the brake rod which in turn was knocking against the floor. And it wasn't moonlight; it was the dawn.

We had just finished a large church in East Sussex. It had been a very successful job. We completely reshingled the spire with our own hand-cleft oak shingles. Several of the locals climbed the spire, all with harnesses and safety lines. The end was celebrated with a superb lunch, all cooked and served in the hall nearby. I was asked to talk to the local Brownies and told them the story of the sheep under the caravan. Then we were asked by the architect to have a look at the neighbouring church.

This church was situated about one and a half miles from the village and, with the exception of a large nursing home, there were no houses for what seemed miles around. Even the nursing home was about half a mile away. It was a very lonely church. At the gateway to the very large churchyard there was a stone building, where I am told they used to sort bones for reburial.

The church was a small stone building with very powerful buttresses supporting the squat tower, topped with a Sussex broached spire. The interior of the church was quite bear with no fixed pews, just a lot of chairs. It is believed that there has been a place of worship on this site since Roman times, but looking at the dimensions of the tower I would have thought Norman with a Victorian spire. There must have been a much older spire, as the weathervane is probably the oldest that I have ever seen or worked on.

As this was a small spire, I decided to shingle it mostly on my own. It was being re-covered in our hand-cleft oak shingles, which are very easy to fix and should not cause any problems. I had my caravan parked behind the bone shed, where there was a toilet with running water. As it was mid-summer time, after work I could sit out and talk to the very friendly locals. There were several regular dog walkers who I got friendly with and were a great help.

One old chap (about the same age as myself) told me that at the time he was churchwarden, he had been at an evening service when he had seen this monk walk down the aisle towards the chancel and disappear. He said that nobody believed him and thought it was his age. As I was staying on site he asked if I would keep a lookout for him. I spoke about this to Keith and Jane, 'Three Dogs', two of the locals, and they agreed that it was probably dementia.

After a couple of weeks the job was progressing well and the weather was exceptionally hot. I was lying in my caravan, tossing and turning. It was too hot to sleep, so I got up and walked across to the church. It was a bright moonlit night, the moonlight creating strong shadows. I could understand why, if you were of a nervous disposition, you could easily imagine seeing things. I went into the church. There were no lights, but with the moonlight shining through the windows it was possible to see enough.

I sat on a seat at the back, near the aisle. The seats weren't in rows, but scattered about haphazardly. I sat there thinking about life in general and a few personal problems. It was a great place to sit and think, it was dark with just enough light to shuffle around between the chairs and very quiet and peaceful.

As I sat there thinking, I looked at a chair quite near to me and thought: "I don't remember that chair being there, but it must have been." So I carried on with my thoughts. A little while later I looked at the chair again. It was closer. This is when you feel a shiver run down your spine. I wasn't afraid of meeting the monk or friar but sitting in the twilight, in an ancient church, in the small hours of the morning, I began to feel apprehensive. So I got up, mumbling something like "Goodnight, friar!" and went back to my caravan.

I got into my bed and was lying there thinking about the chair moving and what the churchwarden had told me about seeing the monk walking or floating down the aisle. As I lay there, quietly thinking, I could hear breathing. I thought I must be listening to my own breathing. I held my breath for as long as I could and I could still hear someone breathing. I tried this – holding my breath – several times, but could still hear breathing. So I sat up in bed and said, "I don't know who you are, but I wish you no harm! And would you please speak or go away!" The next thing I knew it was morning.

Generally on this job it was very peaceful at night, just me and a few animals. They weren't affected by me at all and I could get a sound night's sleep, but there were occasions when suddenly in the middle of the night the church burglar alarm would go off, making an awful noise. But as there was nobody living nearby, nobody heard it except me. As it could only be triggered by movement inside the church I wondered if sometimes youngsters got in there, setting the alarm off to frighten me. A couple of times when this happened I went over to the church and looked inside, but never saw any youngsters or the friar.

Sometimes while staying here at night I would look out across the vast churchyard and there would be a strange phenomenon where you could see everything quite clearly but in a strange light. If you looked carefully you could see this light hovering above certain graves. Wandering around trying to understand this, I noticed that it was only the very oldest graves that the light hovered over and not any of the newest. Well, we have all read or seen films about zombies, the living dead, and of course creeping about a churchyard with a lot of ancient graves, with a torch, reading the inscriptions in the middle of the night, the imagination runs riot. I had read somewhere that ancient bone gives off this phosphorus light, but I spent some time looking and never saw anything or anybody so I went back to bed.

A few years earlier we had been working on this old church in Kent. It was another church where the village was miles away. We were told that the villagers had moved away during the time of the plague. There are often stories like that but you never know the truth.

When we started working on this church it was wintertime. The days were short, getting dark very early. We had our caravan parked behind the church in the car park. The tap for water was situated in the churchyard about a hundred yards or so from the caravan. On the first night I volunteered to go and get the water. It was a strange place with a lot of yew trees and on this particular night it was really windy. What with the trees blowing about and the dark, not the best job in the world.

I took a torch and a container and went over to the tap. As you need one hand to hold the container and one hand to turn the tap on, I turned the torch off while filling the can. As I was just about to pick up the torch, somebody came walking along the path. I said "Good evening!" loudly, so as not to make him jump. He totally ignored me and carried on down the path. I returned to the caravan and mentioned it to my mates, then thought no more of it until the next morning. One of the men followed the path just to see where it went and was surprised when he found it was sealed; there was no way through. This worried both my men and they didn't want to go for water after dark. I spoke to the vicar, who said that many years ago the path led to near the village but had now been sealed off for many years and only led to the graveyard.

I was far more curious than my men and volunteered to get the water every night after dark. I would go over to the tap at approximately the same time every night. Sure enough, along came the fellow – and as I was waiting, hoping to see him again, I was ready with the torch. I shone the torch straight at him, or at where I thought he should be going by the footsteps – absolutely nothing. I tried this every night and most nights I would hear his footsteps on the path, but when I shone the torch I saw nothing.

This whole thing started to intrigue me. I had assumed that these footsteps had gone down the path towards the churchyard. The next night I waited under the yew trees, out of sight. Sure enough, I heard the slight noise of footsteps. I hadn't listened to them before. They were a much lighter tread than we would have made so I was now sure that it was not one of my men playing tricks on me. I listened to where I thought the footsteps had gone and when I walked round, it seemed that whoever was walking around was disappearing by the tower. It was rather odd that in the corner, where the side aisle meets the tower, there was a gravestone, half buried under the tower wall and half led into the footpath. I went back to the tap, picked up my water container and went back to the caravan.

I asked some of the locals and heard all sorts of stories of how they always avoided the churchyard after dark and as there were plague graves, it was a very unhappy place to be after sunset. I never thought much about it after that and just got on with the job, but for some reason I always got the water at lunch time.

After we had completed the work at this church we moved on to another church near Brighton. This was another shingling job, just re-covering the spire with cedar shingles. It was a fairly modern church without many problems. We had been there for about two weeks. I was staying in my caravan on site, but the men were staying in town so they didn't have to drink and drive.

I had settled down for the evening and was just sitting thinking about work and the job in hand, when I started thinking about the last job and the water tap and the footpath and the strange grave. I suddenly got the urge to go back there again, but as it was about a hundred miles away I quickly put the idea out of my head and started to read. The book I was reading at the time wasn't that intriguing and I started thinking about the last job again. I kept thinking about it for a while, then tried reading again. However I kept coming back to wondering whose footsteps they were and where they had disappeared to by the tower. Then, knowing it was completely stupid, I put down my book, locked up the caravan, got into my van and drove back to the last job.

About two and a half hours later I arrived back in the car park where we had parked our caravan. It was pitch dark and there was a very strong wind blowing. The yew trees were swaying about; it was altogether a very uninviting place. I sat there in my van thinking, "What a fool!", but as I was here I should at least have a quick look around. I glanced at the dashboard clock as I got out of the van and thought, "Just a quick look around then back to the caravan."

I walked over to the churchyard and up to where the tap was. I then wandered around the path to where the grave was. Nothing. I started to walk back towards the tap and my van. As I was passing a large gravestone a man suddenly stood up behind the grave and looked straight at me.

What was so strange was that it was dark yet I could see him clearly. He was wearing a wide-brimmed hat with long curly hair, more like ringlets. He had what looked like a frock coat, with gaiters. We stood there looking at each other, not speaking. Although we never spoke, we seemed to communicate. He was lost and didn't want to be there. I immediately thought of the Jewish cemetery at Canterbury, because he looked as if that's where he belonged. I felt uneasy. I felt that he wanted me to go with him, so I headed back to the van. I glanced back once, but he had gone. I got into the van and locked the door. I had only been gone, over at the graveyard, for five minutes at the most, but when I looked at the dashboard clock I had been there for one and a half hours.

On the drive back to my caravan I pondered about this old man with his strange clothing, and I seemed to know a lot about him. I knew that he and his family had lived there long ago but had been forced to move to Canterbury, where they had a synagogue, but some of them were still here in this graveyard and he was trying to put things right.

I still think about him occasionally and wonder. Was he a ghost? Or just some old man with dementia wandering about at night? Or was it my vivid imagination playing tricks with me? I like to think I was very lucky to meet him and I hope we meet again, perhaps in some other churchyard.

It is well known that I am interested in all churches and always stop and look around any church I happen to pass. I was driving through East Sussex when, as I was passing a small stone church, I had this urge to stop and walk around. I parked my van and walked around the churchyard looking at the graves and reading the gravestones. A very pretty church, -- so I sat on a grave and started to sketch the church. I finished my drawing and went on my way. It was only later that night, when I was going through the events of the day that I looked at my pad and realised that I had drawn the old man. It was only a rough sketch and where I had done the shading it was quite clear that the old man was there. Perhaps my imagination was running wild.

Another church where there were unexplained occurrences was in Kent, but nearer to London. This church was situated at the end of a long country road. There were no houses around, just the church and a few dog walkers. I had my caravan parked very close to the churchyard. I like to park as close as I can to connect to the electricity. There were three of us working on this church. It was a complete re-shingle with cedar. My two mates were not staying in the caravan with me. They were travelling to this job daily.

I usually go to bed early, but on this occasion I stayed up to watch a programme being broadcast from Jerusalem and as part of the commentary was in Hebrew I managed to stay awake. The programme finished at about one o'clock and I was just settling down for the night when I heard this baby crying. As this church and my caravan were a good half mile from the nearest house I could not understand what anyone would be doing out at this time of night, especially with a baby. I listened for a while and then heard it again. I got up and looked through the curtains but could see nothing. I went back to bed thinking I must have been mistaken and it was a mixture of my imagination and the wind. I woke up some time later and heard the baby crying again. This time I listened very carefully and could hear a woman's voice chiding a baby. I don't know how long I listened, but I went back to sleep – for the next thing I knew it was morning and time to get up before the men returned.

After breakfast and before the men turned up I had a walk around the churchyard. Over in the corner there was a fairly recent, very small grave, still with a lot of flowers covering it – but at the lower end something had disturbed the earth by digging or scratching, leaving part of a little white coffin exposed. I filled the hole with stones and rearranged the earth and flowers and for the next few nights kept one eye open, occasionally going out to look around, hoping to see a fox or badger. I saw neither and heard nothing else. Thankfully it was a short job.

I was in a Hampshire pub one night having a jar or two with a couple of the locals. I went in the pub to ask where the church was. This was a very countrified area and I hadn't seen any sign of a church, but these locals knew it well and gave me directions. I also asked about caravan parking in the area. They told me that there was plenty of room around the church and that nobody would disturb me as local people did not go round there at night. When I enquired why, they told me a story about a stage coach pulled by four horses that would rise out of the small lake opposite the church and cross the road between the church and the lake. They also told me that quite a few people had seen this, but as usual all the folk who had seen this gave a different description and nobody had witnessed this from close quarters.

We finished our drinks and I bought them another round and left to find the church. At this point I only wanted to visit the church to measure up for pricing, but I did have a good look at the lake. It didn't look deep enough to hide a stage coach and four horses, but it was a very lonely place and I could understand why locals didn't come here at night – not the place to run into a coach and four.

I priced the job and sometime later my quote was accepted. I had intended to travel to this job daily, as it was not far away, but I was fascinated by the stories and quite fancied seeing a coach and four that could float. So when we started the job I took my caravan and parked it in front of the church, between the lake and the church. After all, I didn't want the coach driver to miss me! This was only a short job, so I needed to stay every night because I was going to photograph it and show the locals. Every night after work the men went home. I cooked a meal and waited. For four nights I waited -- nothing but a good night's sleep. On the fifth and last night I sat there listening and eventually went to sleep. I was awakened by this awfully loud noise of horses and creaking leather and jingling harnesses. Even though I had been waiting for nearly a week it took me by surprise and by the time I had grabbed my camera, pulled on my trousers and got outside there was nothing but a very dark night. Bitterly disappointed, I went back to bed until morning.

In the morning, as soon as it was light, I went out looking for tracks but: nothing. I walked across the road and stood looking at the lake and couldn't find an explanation for the two muddy lines about five feet apart right across the lake.

Chapter Twelve

Guildford Cathedral

G uildford. In 1964 the main body of the cathedral was completed with the exception of the north and south garths, which were added much later. During 1965 I was repping the area and called in at the cathedral. In those days the offices were not at the cathedral itself but in Quarry Street, so when I called in at the cathedral looking for work one of the guides pointed me in the direction of Alfred White, who was the Dean's Verger. Although he didn't need a steeplejack at that time, saying that it was a new building and they weren't expecting any problems in the near future, he took my card and said he'd remember my name.

About three weeks later I had a phone call from the Dean's Verger asking if I could help. Someone had been up at the cathedral late at night and had pulled the halyards to the top of the flagpoles. Once the halyards have been pulled up, the only way to get them down is to climb the poles. He was hoping I could resolve the problem quickly, as some very important people would be attending the service on Sunday. He didn't say who, but given the number of police searching roof voids, manholes and drains while we were working on the flagpoles I soon had a pretty good idea who would be visiting.

There are two free standing steel poles, fifty feet in height. They are nine inches in diameter at the base reducing to three and a half at the top, where there are very heavy trucks with two sheaves on each pole. Above the trucks the south pole has a crown made from copper and painted and gilded, the north pole has a bishop's mitre. Referring to them as the north and south poles has been the cause of some laughter over the years. They are situated at the west end of the cathedral, in front of the main entrance.

I arrived at the cathedral very early on Saturday morning only to be greeted by the police, who refused me entry. The verger had forgotten to inform the police that I was coming, but after a few phone calls I was allowed to enter and by lunchtime flags were once again flying from both poles. This was the start of a long association with the cathedral.

Just two months later the angel weathervane stuck and we were asked to free it so that it turned to the wind again. This turned out to be quite a job, as the angel weighs about a ton, or 1,000 kilograms in today's money, and the bearing that it turns on is situated high up inside the angel, in its throat. To get to this bearing we would have to lift the angel by almost ten feet in order to clear the pole on which it turns, using only a dolly stick and hand winches. After getting the angel safely onto the tower roof we were able to free the bearing, pack it with grease and replace it back into the throat of the angel.

I was surprised to find the bearing so dry, as this was only 1969 and the angel had only been there since 1964, less than six years. I believed at the time, and still do, that the cuff between the angel's sleeve and robe was not sealed well and so, because the angel always points towards the wind and weather, water was entering and travelling along the inside of the arm and washing grease away from the bearing. We sealed the cuff and the angel turned, without the bearing requiring any further attention, until it was removed for regilding some forty years later.

Around this time the Dean's Verger asked us if we could help with the cathedral's pigeon problem, the problem being there were so many pigeons that the drains and gutters were continuously blocked. We were told the story that someone had donated six hawks to live on the cathedral to keep pigeons at bay, but it seemed that the hawks and pigeons lived quite happily side by side. The hawks only ever ate a pigeon if they were hungry, not killing for the sake of killing. Perhaps man could learn something from these birds.

We were offered a contract to clean out all the gutters and parapets at six month intervals. They already had a building firm doing this, but they were having difficulty reaching some parts of the cathedral. So we started cleaning every six months. It soon became obvious that once every six months was not enough and we started cleaning the gutters every three months, but there were so many pigeons living on this building that we often had to visit in between times.

Over time other problems started to show up, for example damp stains near the crossing, in the southwest corner of the gallery and above the clerestory windows on the south side. Many years and several architects later, the source of this damp was found by monitoring the gutters and roofs over a period of years. We put in ventilators, which also acted as drains for the condensation along the south side of the nave. We removed the stains from the clerestory windows and from the south west stones of the crossing. Most of this internal work was done at night, so as not to disrupt the workings of the cathedral.

The damp to the southwest corner of the west gallery was a completely different problem. I was pretty sure that I knew where and what the problem was, but it was not easy to convince the architects that I was right. At that time we were dealing with both the cathedral architects and with architects from English Heritage, who had differing opinions about the problem. So I had to convince them and the other interested parties that I was right. We erected a scaffold on the inside of the south gallery wall, with access to the corner of the west window, and a couple of my men went outside and sprayed the wall with a power washer to simulate the weather on a bad day. This is a very thick wall, but the architects standing on the scaffolding inside got wet rather quickly from water coming through gaps in the plaster and proving my theory correct: driving rain was penetrating a badly built wall.

It was not until several years later, when we removed the outer part of the wall, that it was possible to see just how many open joints there were on the inner brickwork. The wall was reinstated with a cavity and a waterproof membrane, which seemed to solve the problem. We also lifted the parapet stones on the west gable and the south side of the nave. This was to put copper damp proofing under the stones. On the west nave gable, under the coping stones, there is a time capsule with a few items that should interest workers in the future.

In the early days there was no refectory at the cathedral, just a wooden hut over on the south side. There were actually several huts of different sizes; this one was used by the Women's Institute. They were a very formidable bunch. On one occasion the Dean's Verger was asked, or rather expected, to have afternoon tea with these ladies. I was working on the flag poles at the time and he called me down and asked me to join him, thinking I might help the conversation along. He needn't have worried, as neither of us could get a word in edgeways.

Eventually it was agreed that most of the staining on the cathedral walls was from condensation, but there was also another source and that was water penetrating from the tower. On very wet and windy days water used to run down the spiral staircases until it found cracks and cavities, through which it would seep out of the east wall of the transept. Over time it washed out the lime mortar joints leaving large areas of brickwork without any joints. Several building firms were called in to repoint this area, but they didn't appreciate that the water was coming from the inside and that these joints were not being washed away by driving rain. If one looks at the position of the affected brickwork, it is very sheltered which should have been a clue. This point was argued many times over the years, as nobody seemed to realise that this was a unique building that didn't always conform to general building practices.

It was only later that we got a chance to confirm that water was coming in through the small windows to the staircases and running down the stairs. The bell ringers complained whenever it rained at the weekend, or on practice night. We suggested that the windows should be covered as a temporary measure to test our theory. This was rather reluctantly agreed to, so we made up some frames from lead and perspex. These frames were not really in keeping with the building, but they proved our point and are still there many years later. I just hope there is a record of this before somebody decides to take them down and starts the whole process all over again.

Over my time at the cathedral there have been five different architects. One of the most conscientious was Tony di'Corsi. We spent many hours together sitting up in the roof voids, watching water come in and following its path down into the building. He really wanted to cure all the problems, no matter how much effort was required. I remember one morning receiving a phone call from Tony asking me to meet him at the cathedral because a new problem had arisen. I turned up at the cathedral but couldn't find him. I asked at the office, but they hadn't seen him. I found the verger, who had seen Tony some time earlier in the nave. I was a little concerned, as I knew that he was not well.

I went into the cathedral at the west end and looked around the narthex, where we had last talked about the ingress of water. Then I went through to the nave and looked down the aisle towards the crossing. About a third of the way down the aisle was Tony, lying on his back in a very awkward position and not moving. I was really worried. I thought he had had a heart attack and died. He didn't move as I approached, calling his name. But he did move and sat up when I poked him with my toe. I then realised that he was holding a pair of binoculars and studying the ceiling. After I'd welcomed him back to the land of the living he told me that a large piece of concrete had fallen from one of the ribs in the roof void and landed on the vaulting. The vaulting is only about three and a half inches thick, so even though it is reinforced Tony was worried that it might have been cracked.

It turned out that the falling concrete had not damaged the vaulting, but Tony remained concerned about possible movement of the building. It was well known that at the west end of the nave the north and south walls were built slightly out of upright, but the west end of the nave also leans slightly out of upright. Tony's concern was whether this was also leaning intentionally or if it moved because of concrete expanding, which might also have caused the concrete on the rib to spall. There is a section of roof towards the west end of the nave that is made of a different material. It had always been assumed that this was there to allow for any expansion, but there doesn't appear to be any sort of expansion joint in the dwarf side wall that supports the nave roof.

At the other end of the nave, where the east nave roof butts against the tower, there was also a serious problem. It was just before Christmas and the vergers were getting the cathedral ready for the celebrations when large pieces if mortar appeared on the floor below the west crossing arch. The first thought was to get scaffolders in, but scaffolding would have completely ruined the view from the nave to the choir and altar. The vergers asked if we could help.

First we ran ladders up the walls under the arch, then more ladders following the arch to the apex. Once the ladders were in place we could inspect the arch at close quarters, even though we were hanging almost upside down. It appeared that where the arch abuts the tower there was a gap approximately two inches wide and that the builders had filled this gap with mortar. This mortar had become very dry and had started to break up and fall out. From looking at the brickwork on the outside it seemed clear that the nave had moved. We erected temporary covers under the arch to catch any mortar, but it must have looked rather strange to members of the congregation looking up from their prayers to see an array of ladders and a great big blob of green tarpaulin. We were asked to fill the gap between the tower and the nave roof with polystyrene. The cathedral gave us a strip of polystyrene to go into the gap. I assumed at the time that this was just a temporary measure, but I wouldn't be surprised if it's still there.

Chapter Thirteen

Isolated Instances

We were working on a church near Hever Castle in Kent. It was a typical village church, not very tall but a nice peaceful job. It was mid-summer and the weather was good, so sometimes after work and a bit of a clean-up we went to the local pub for a drink. Most times we would sit outside in the peaceful surroundings, but on this particular day a crowd of young Hooray Henrys and Henryesses turned up and certainly ruined the peace. They really didn't cause us any problems and it was interesting listening to them all trying to outdo each other. As we sat there watching, one of our younger chaps couldn't take his eyes off one of the girls. "Why don't you try your luck?" I asked. "A bird like that would never look at me!" he said.

I told him that he had as good a chance as anyone. It was just a matter of how you put it over. I pointed to a big glass ashtray on the table where they we sitting and suggested he should just saunter casually over towards their table, 'spot' the

ashtray, pick it up and say something like: "Wow, this is a
lucky find! It's lead crystal and if you hold it up to the light
you can see all the colours of the spectrum." This would really
impress her, I told him. "'My goodness', she'll think, he knows
his stuff, he must be an antiques dealer", and would start
talking to him about antiques. He said that he'd consider my
suggestion. We left it at that and carried on with our own
conversation.

A few days later we were sitting outside the same public
house when the bunch of noisy Hooray Henrys appeared. Well,
our young lad had talked of nothing else but this girl, boring
the rest of us almost to tears. "Now's your chance," I said as
the fellows went inside to buy the drinks. After a bit of jollying
along he got up and sauntered over to their table.

He was a funny little chap who walked a bit like Charlie
Chaplin, but he waddled over and was passing their table when
he suddenly stopped and did a double take on the ashtray, then
picked it up and looked at if closely. "This is a very rare item,"

he told the girl, "it's made of lead, and if you hold it up to the light you can see all the colours of the scrotum." The chaps turned up with the drinks and heard our lad's final remarks, putting an end to any chance of romance.

Even though by this time we were specialising in church repair work, we still got asked to take on some industrial contracts. One of these was a brick chimney on an airfield. This chimney was situated in the middle of the boiler house roof and projected about fifty to sixty feet above the roof. We laddered the chimney and erected a small scaffolding deck around the top. Another boiler was being added, which meant adding a flue. Because the chimney was square on plan and there wasn't enough room for two flues, the powers that be decided to take out the Molar firebrick liner and just let the existing boiler discharge straight into the stack.

We had chairs rigged on the inside ready to start when the boiler man called up to us. He told us that he was going to be working on the existing boiler, but not to worry as it shouldn't interfere with us. We got into our chairs. There were only two of us, as the third man who would normally keep an eye on things below had not turned up. We had barely started when I looked down and saw a big black cloud of smoke coming up the chimney. I shouted to my mate that the boiler man had flashed up the boiler. Talk about panic! We were trying to pull ourselves up and get out while holding our breath. We managed to reach the deck and the black cloud of smoke suddenly stopped. That didn't make sense.

I was on my way down to give the boiler man a piece of my mind when he came out to see what all the noise was about. It turned out that he hadn't flashed up the boiler at all, but had turned on a fan to test it and this had blown deposited soot back up the chimney. After that we made him find something else to do and locked the boiler house, which is what we should have done in the first place.

Some years ago I had repaired some handrails on a dredger off the coast near Littlehampton. That's not really the type of work we like to do, so I had almost forgotten about it and was very surprised when after all the intervening years we got a new enquiry from the operators. One of their sand pits was closing and they were removing all their equipment. Down at the lower level they had sunk three shafts. The idea was to lower the water level so that they could extract the sand. These were steel shafts, two feet six inches in diameter, about a hundred feet deep from the pit floor. During the excavations there had been pumps at the bottom of these shafts which had kept the water table lower than the working area.

When excavations were completed they had removed the pumps, so only a limited time remained before the water table rose and eventually flooded the pit. They were using their own staff to remove the equipment but were having great trouble trying to get the steel shafts out. The company had supplied them with shear legs, powerful winches and fifty ton hydraulic jacks. They had rigged this equipment up over one of the shafts, but nothing was moving. The company needed shafts for another pit and they were enormously expensive. After about a week of trying to reclaim those shafts and on the point of abandoning them, someone had remembered us.

We arrived on site with a lot of our own equipment and decided that we would re-rig the shear legs and lower a man down to cut the bottoms of the shafts. That's where the fixings for the pumps were located and we thought that was what was holding the shaft. One problem was that the shaft diameter of two feet six inches was about the same as distance from the knees to the behind of a man sitting on a bosun's chair, so we made a special round bosun's chair upon which a man could stand as we lowered him down the shaft.

There was some arguing about who should go down. An expression sometimes used when someone is forced to do something they don't really want to is that they're getting shafted. Perhaps this is where that started. As it had been my idea, I volunteered. It was quite claustrophobic on the way down. It was all right until someone put their head over to look down, blocking the light. Then you feel you can't breathe, but I am sure most of it is in the mind. Once at the bottom it became obvious what was causing the problem: the bottom section had been damaged when it was driven down years earlier. We lowered down some burning gear and took turns, each of us only working for a short time. At least we could use the winch to ride up and down the shaft.

As soon as we had chopped off the offending bit at the bottom, we hooked the winch to the top of the shaft and fitted the two fifty ton hydraulic jacks ready to lift. Nothing moved. The shaft was still stuck fast. We had several sheave blocks in our van so we uncoupled the winch and reeved up several blocks, ending up with about five or six. We then recoupled the winch, pumped up the jacks and started to pull. Nothing moved. I grabbed hold of the winch operating rope and began snatching the winch. That probably didn't do the winch much good, but all of a sudden the shaft started to move, just an inch or so. After we adjusted the jacks and tried again there was a lot more movement and soon we had raised the shaft sufficiently to clamp the second section and remove the first. We felt great.

The sand pit was deep and large. Part of it was flooded, like a small lake. It was a beautiful sunny February day and the reflection of the sky made the lake look so blue that I decided to go for a swim. I stripped off down to my pants, went to the edge and jumped in. Burning at the bottom of the shaft earlier might have been taking a chance, but jumping into that water was definitely the most stupid thing I had done all day. It was icy cold and I couldn't climb back onto the bank I'd jumped off. One of our chaps came to the edge to help me, but the bank gave way and he too got soaked. The others stood there, laughing, and I had a very uncomfortable ride home.

We had looked after one church in Hampshire for many years. They had a very severe woodpecker problem and every few years we would go back and repair the damaged shingles. On this particular occasion we were asked to ladder and inspect the spire with a view to reshingling it. I asked if we could fix our ladders on Saturday morning ready to start the job on Monday. At first they weren't too happy with the idea, but they agreed as long as we could be finished by lunchtime.

On the Saturday morning we arrived at about eight o'clock with our ladders and equipment and parked in front of the church. One of our men, who hadn't been with us very long, asked me if he could ladder the spire. Normally I like to do the laddering myself, but on this occasion and as there were permanent fixings I agreed and left him and his mate to it. He was to do the fixing and his mate would carry the ladders for him. I watched as they laddered the tower and everything seemed okay. Then they started on the spire, which would normally worry me as it is not always easy to get a good fixing into shingles. But in this instance I knew there were permanent fixings that we had put in ten years before, so I got started sorting out the ropes and other equipment.

It must have been about an hour later when I stood back to look up and see how they were getting on. They were about to put the second to last ladder on and seemed to be doing everything right. I watched as they fitted the ladder into the sleeves of the one below. The ladderer was fixing the first tie and was really banging the ladder when the tie suddenly came loose and the ladder came back with the man on it. I heard him scream and then go silent. I think he blacked out. I could only watch as he fell, both him and the ladder disappearing from sight into the valley gutter of the nave roof below-- silence. The second man climbed down and peered over the ridge into the gutter. He shouted down that his mate was either dead or unconscious. I ran to the vicarage to use a phone, but they had already called an ambulance – they had been watching us work and seen the man fall.

I ran back to the church and we put ladders over the roof to get to him. I climbed over the roof and reached the man with his ladder. He was still alive, but not conscious. At that moment the ambulance arrived. Two paramedics climbed up but could not reach him. Then the fire and rescue service turned up with their specialist equipment. They put the injured man into a sort of straitjacket and, with a lot of struggling, got him down to ground level. Then the police turned up as well. It seems that they automatically attend any accident to which the other emergency services are called. So we had an unconscious man, a fire engine, an ambulance and the police all parked in front of the church when the bride turned up. I had forgotten all about finishing early and clearing the churchyard by lunchtime.

You hear stories about a bride turning up first, or see scenes in films where she has to drive round the block. In this case she would have been better taking a turn round the M25. Our man was still unconscious when he left the site, but we heard from the hospital later that he was all right and he returned to work two days later calling himself Tumbledown Jack. He had a couple of broken fingers and a few cracked ribs. I would have thought that a near miss like that would have steadied him a bit, but no such luck. He's still as reckless as ever, from what I hear and read about him.

On this particular church I think we were lucky that we got away so lightly without anybody getting badly hurt. About ten years before this fall we had been engaged in repairing the shingles. Once again the woodpeckers had been busy pecking holes. Only myself and one man had gone there as it should have been a relatively short, easy job. As we laddered the spire we realised that we were not getting any good fixings. The boarding was very thin and our fixings didn't really have enough purchase, but we carried on, putting extra fixings in and praying with everything crossed.

As we neared the top I realised that we were short of ladders. Now there was no excuse for this as we had laddered this spire several times before, so I was entirely to blame. I didn't want to go back to the yard as this was supposed to be a short job and I hadn't allowed much time on it. As well as repairing the shingling, the church had asked us to inspect the weather cockerel and the iron finial. We run out of ladders some eight feet from the apex, just below the very deep lead apron. This should have given us a clue that the top might be unsafe, as it should have been obvious that repairs had been carried out to the top of the spire. You learn over the years that if there have been repairs, the chances are that they were temporary and not meant to stand the test of time.

Our ladders had finished about eight feet from the weathervane. I had managed to fit a wire lashing around the spire at this point, so the poor fixings were no longer a worry. I climbed up and stood on the top rung with my arms wrapped around the spire. I could just reach the lead boss, which was a large oak ball some 12" in diameter covered in lead. This lead was original and was probably 8lb (per square foot) when new, but it had weathered down somewhat so wasn't quite as heavy.

But I could not reach the finial or the weathervane, so I stood on the sleeves of the ladder – still not enough to reach. At this point we were only trying to get the weathervane down and inspect the finial and cap, so we didn't need to erect a platform, just get high enough to reach and lift the cockerel off his perch.

My mate, who had been running the ladders, came up with the idea that if I stood on the top rung of the ladders and wrapped my arms around the spire he could climb up my back, stand on my shoulders and be able to reach the weather cockerel. So that's what he did. He climbed up, nearly throttling me as he used my neck to steady himself, stood on my shoulders and shouted that he could reach the weather cockerel but it was heavier than he thought and he was frightened he might drop it. I had some polypropylene rope ties, so I told him to tie one of them onto the cockerel and I would tie the end to my belt, I didn't think it was long enough to tie to the spire with enough slack. I told him to lift the cockerel off its perch and pass it to me.

After much swearing and grunting he finally got it off and was lowering it down to me when the finial started to move towards the west.

All this time he was standing on my shoulders (very painful) and now I had the cockerel hanging from my belt, with one arm around the spire and the other trying to hold the cockerel so that I could tie it to the wire lashing that was around the spire. I asked my mate: "How safe is the finial?" He said he was not very happy, as it was swaying quite alarmingly and seemed to have come unfixed just below the lead-covered ball. He didn't know what to do, as he had felt it move as he used it to climb up. I told him that he was hurting my bony shoulder and that his feet smelled. I told him I would try to climb down the ladders with him on my shoulders until he could reach the top rung. I also told him not to put any weight on the finial as he slowly climbed down.

The next day, after talking to the church, we erected a scaffolding around the top and opened up the lead. It was amazing. All the timber around the top of the spire was rotten and there was no vane rod supporting the finial. This was definitely a case of the weathervane staying in place just by the force of habit.

One thing you should always remember in this job is never to brag about anything, because it always comes back to bite you. I should have remembered that on a job in Aldershot. We had been asked by the Ministry of Works to look at the Army's training course for physical training instructors. Apparently all the tree walks, death slides and abseils had been neglected for several years. They wanted them to be upgraded and a couple of scaffolding structures needed renewing. They had several drawings for these structures, but at least one was missing. I had done a drawing for the construction of a footbridge some years before and thought that I could reproduce the missing drawings.

After a lot of trouble I produced drawings for the structures to their approval and we were asked to carry out the work, which consisted of rebuilding the scaffold structures and building new roped access with wire slides. All this was done under the watchful eye of a senior officer. Once we had completed the job and were about to leave, the officer said "It looks all right, but as you erected it you should be the first to try it out." My mate didn't fancy riding on any of it, so it was left to me. I thoroughly enjoyed it, even though some of the equipment was a little hairy.

Before leaving the camp we were invited to join some of the trainees in the NAAFI for a cup of tea and a chat. Some of them wanted to know what other jobs we had done. At some point during the conversation I told them about my short time working as a rigger for Bertram Mills's circus. I recalled how during that time I had helped with rigging the trapeze and had even tried my hand at catching. One of the trainees asked why I hadn't tried flying. I told him that I hadn't really had an opportunity, as I was only a rigger and the trapeze artistes did all the clever stuff.

It turned out that the chap asking all the questions came from a family of circus performers who had specialised in trapeze. He said that even though I had missed a golden opportunity to experience the wonder of flying from a trapeze, all was not lost. He had trapezes fixed up at the military swimming pool and if I wanted to accompany them one afternoon he would give me some training in the art of flying. We arranged a date and time to meet at the swimming pool.

On that fateful day I met him and after changing we climbed up into the roof space above the pool, where there were two trapezes rigged up, one at each end of the pool. There were two very small platforms, one for each trapeze. The trainee PTI got on to his platform and I scrambled on to the other one. He told me to get hold of the bar and swing out and back again to land on my little platform. He told me to do this several times to get the feel for it. He said if I kept swinging he would throw his trapeze, which I could catch and then swing back to land on his platform. He told me not to worry and to leave the timing up to him.

The first couple of times I couldn't quite reach, but I kept swinging backwards and forwards and he kept swinging the empty trapeze. After a while he shouted "This time!" and I swung out over the pool and grabbed the other bar at the same time as letting go of my trapeze. The next thing I knew, I shot down into the pool, coughing and spluttering for breath. What he hadn't told me was that the second trapeze was on bungee ropes. I think every soldier in Aldershot had been told, however, as an awful lot of them suddenly appeared, having a great laugh at my expense. I learned that day that you should keep your mouth shut and not brag about what you have done before.

Somewhere around 1980 we were asked to shingle a spire at Hadlow. While we were working on the church I often used to look up at the tower next door. It was a strange building and there were many stories about why it was there. Almost everybody referred to the building as Hadlow Castle, although it is not really a castle at all but a folly. I believe that its proper name is May's Folly, built for a gentleman named May in the nineteenth century as a symbol of his wealth. It is said that it was built with a very tall tower so that wherever his estranged wife went with her new lover she would see the tower and realise just what she had thrown away. The story goes that when old May died he was buried standing upright in his tomb in the churchyard and that when eventually his corpse decayed and collapsed, so would the tower. As we would eventually work on the tower I hope that his remains are fully supported.

As our work on the church was coming to an end, the owner of the tower came by and asked about some repair work. He invited me to visit the castle so that we could climb the tower together and discuss the work. As we climbed the tower I looked at how this strange structure was supported. I came to the conclusion that some, if not all of the tower only stayed standing from force of habit, maybe just waiting for old May's corpse to fall in on itself in the tomb next door. After we had completed our climb and admired the fantastic view of the Kentish Weald from the top of the tower, we discussed the work and the owner said that he would be in touch.

One Sunday morning sometime later I had a phone call from the new owner of the castle. He had only just bought it and recently moved in when a severe storm badly damaged the tower. The church next door had given him my name: could I help? I drove down the next day and was amazed at the amount of damage I could see. As I approached the castle, two of the pinnacles from the top of the lantern were missing and the entire balustrade from the link (a walkway joining the top of the stair turret to the lantern) had been smashed. I wondered about the occupied property at the base of the tower.

As I drove in, the new owner of the castle came out to greet me. He told me that one of the missing pinnacles had fallen through the roof, smashing the staircase up to the lantern, so there was now no way of getting up to the top to see how safe things were. I said that I would try to get up there to check. I went up the stone staircase as far as the link. Although balustrade had been totally destroyed, with great care I could still get across and enter the tower. Once inside I could see that the staircase to the lantern and tower roof were also totally destroyed. There certainly was no safe way of getting up to the top. I came down and spoke to the owner again. I told him that to reach the tower roof I would need to get ladders and equipment and bring a couple of men, to which he agreed.

The next morning we turned up with our equipment, climbed up to the link and dropped down a rope which we then used to haul up a number of ladders. We passed the ladders through the small doorway into the tower and started fixing them up through the floor openings left by the collapsed staircase. As we got higher I began to realise just how dangerous this whole building was and to wonder just how we could support it. Eventually we got our ladders high enough to open the hatch out on to the flat roof.

What we saw made me wonder what was preventing the whole lantern from collapsing. One pinnacle had gone – the one that had smashed the staircase – and another was hanging over the edge, held only by a small piece of metal that was actually part of the lightning protection system. Three others were also leaning so badly that only the thin aluminium lightning tape was holding them in place. All of this on top of a very flimsy, 50 foot high rendered brickwork lantern – which itself sits on a 120 foot tower.

We left everything untouched and came back down. I told the owner that we could not touch anything until the lantern was properly supported. He got in touch with his insurers, who agreed that we should do the job. The next day I purchased a large quantity of scaffolding which we started to erect on top of the tower, around the base of the lantern. It was a slow, laborious job because we knew that vibrations could easily bring everything down around us. Once the scaffolding was in place and properly braced, we lowered the most dangerous pinnacle to the ground and fixed temporary supports to make the others safe.

The owner engaged engineers to survey the tower. With our assistance they climbed up to the base of the lantern, getting more despondent about the condition of the brickwork and the timber construction with every step. They refused to go any higher than the base of the lantern despite the fact that it was supported. It was at this point that the insurance company decided that they had paid out enough to cover their contractual obligations and would not be releasing any more money. The following year, 1987, saw the Great Storm sweep across the country. It blew over an estimated 15 million trees and did untold damage to numerous buildings, but did not manage to cause any fresh damage to the castle, so we must have got the support scaffold about right.

The building stayed as it was for around eight years, with no insurance cover for the people living in the houses around the base of the tower, until the local council stepped in and retained us to carry out regular inspections. Eventually we were given the go-ahead to dismantle the lantern and all the pinnacles. We had to number each brick and stack in readiness for the rebuild. With the tower now weatherproof and safe, the council could start the job of resolving ownership and funding issues. That was a process that would take many years.

Taking the lantern and the pinnacles down, together with other loose or dangerous features, was a very easy job. Every brick could simply be lifted off the lime mortar, which had rotted out completely and offered no adhesion at all. We had a powered hoist to lower the numbered bricks, to be stacked for reuse, and the rubble.

We stacked a great many bricks and had a bit of a laugh at some of them, which had drawings reminiscent of Pompeii. They were from the pencils of the fire watchers who used to sit up on the tower during the last war, sometimes all night, and on quiet nights sketched to stave off the boredom.

Although the tower has since been rebuilt, it will never be the same in my eyes. Usually when you visit a historic building, you look at the stones and arches and think about the people who built them and about their lives. But once a building has been demolished, or in this case deconstructed, what is rebuilt is essentially new. It may be something that later generations will ponder.

Chapter Fourteen

To Shingle a Spire

As I travel around the country I always look at every church I pass. If the spire has recently been reshingled then I always stop, take my binoculars and have a really good look. I can often work out which contractor carried out the work, mainly by the style of shingling. We all have our funny little quirks that make each job individual. I look at each job carefully, looking for the tell-tale signs that most of us leave so proudly.

As I have always championed the church, I look at all the jobs that I see with a very critical eye and think to myself that I could or would have done it better (my opinion only) and over the next few pages I shall try to explain how I think a church spire should be reshingled.

When a spire gets to the stage where there is no alternative but to recover completely, this has usually been picked up by the church's architect at the last quinquennial inspection. There are all the problems of getting permissions, faculties etc. and of course, trying to satisfy the purists, what type of shingles should be used.

I think that when decisions are being made the best rule of thumb is to try and check back to find what the original covering was, which is not too difficult if the date of the building is known. For instance, a timber spire built between the fifteenth century and the start of the twentieth century would have been covered with oak, or in the more country and wooded areas some would have been covered with hand-cleft sweet chestnut. The difference in appearance once they have weathered is negligible and the life expectancy is about the same.

Although there is an enormous difference between the cost of manufacturing oak and chestnut shingles, chestnut being the cheaper of the two, it was thought that on the grander and more important churches such as in the towns and cities (their opinion, not mine) it was more prestigious to use the more expensive material. This also applied to thatch many years ago.

Generally speaking from 1939 onwards the vast majority were covered with western red cedar shingles.

It's not too difficult for the architect to work out what the correct covering should be, but of course there's always the problem of funding. Once the problems of funding and pleasing everyone have been overcome, the architect can then prepare his specification for the work. This is where in a lot of cases things start to go wrong. The bulk of the specification is virtually the same, just repeated on each job, and doesn't cause too many problems, but when you get to the back section (the "Works") things can go wrong.

Architects, in my opinion have, so much work to do with raising funds, getting the permissions, trying to please the authorities and all the preliminaries of the specifications that they don't put enough details into the Works. Another problem is when the architect doesn't insist that the contractor has at least one man on site, usually the foreman, who has been trained in church spire shingling. The next big problem is access. The access itself is not a problem, it is how it is carried out that is the problem!

I believe that all accesses should comply with all safety requirements in place at the time, but it is the interpretation of the regulations – everyone seems to interpret them to suit their own ideas. My ideal way on a typical broach spire is to run ladders up to the apex where chairs and safety lines can be attached. We try to always ladder to the nave roof where it butts against the tower. Using a bosun's chair we fix tubes on each side of the ladder, passing short tubes under the ladder fixed to these tubes which are saddled over the ridge. This is a good fixing for the ladders and also allows room for your feet on the rungs. From these tubes we punch short standards and fix handrails both sides of the ladders. We do this from the gutter to the nave ridge, with a class 1 extension ladder from the ground to the gutter fixed with two ringed rawls which are left in place for the duration of the job. This allows the extension ladder to be removed when the site is left unattended.

From the ridge up to the base of the spire we encase the vertical ladder with a scaffolding tower. Around the complete church tower we erect a scaffolding platform suspended from steel brackets and/or certified wires. This is fully boarded, hand railed and enclosed with debris netting. We then shingle the spire to a height of about six feet including the broaches.

At this point, if okayed after inspection by the architect, we carry on shingling using bosun's chairs up to approximately ten to fifteen feet from the apex. We then fix a square on plan scaffolding, which we extend to the top with progress.

If the inspecting architect is not happy climbing our ladders, we enclose them with a scaffold tower up to the top scaffolding.

A TYPICAL WORKS SPECIFICATION FOR SHINGLING

- After access has been gained, strip all old shingles in about six foot bands around the spire and provide temporary covers.
- Clean down the close boarding and thoroughly check for worm and rot. Also check the thickness of the board and that there are sufficient gaps between to allow air to circulate.
- When replacing with traditional oak shingles the boarding needs to be a minimum of 1"; if re-covering with cedar, the boarding can stay at ¾" thick.
- Re-nail the boards with stainless steel nails; two nails to each board, each rafter. The nails should be of a heavy gauge with ring shanks.
- The tilting fillet should be two layers of 7" or 8" feather edge tanalised soft wood. Using this feather edge eliminates the gap behind the shingles where insects like to live.
- Start the shingles with a minimum of 2" overhanging the tilting fillets. There should be a double course to start with. The shingles should have a side lap of at least 2".
- The shingles if oak or chestnut should be laid in 4" (100mm) courses. This gauge should not be exceeded over the complete spire. If the course needs to be adjusted then this should be done by reducing the exposure.
- As soon as possible, a level line should be drawn around the spire. Just above the broaches is probably the best place to draw this line. All measurements for the courses should be measured from this line. On larger spires it is much more accurate to use a water level to draw this line.
- It usually pays to shingle the four panels first. The panels are the facets on the cardinal elevations. These are shingled up as far as is comfortable from the eaves scaffolding. The important thing when shingling these panels is cutting the shingle to follow the line of the hip. Lay a straight edge across the broach and that is the line you should cut to. No shingle on the panel should foul this straight edge.

- To start shingling the broaches, mark a line on the panel shingles and lay a shingle to follow this line, then trim it again using the straight edge. Fix a shingle on the broach and on top of the hip, shingle and trim to suit.
- Once the first course to the broach is laid, a stainless steel soaker should be laid over the shingles and turned down over the hip. This soaker is only necessary between the double courses at the start of the broach, although we often put a soaker across the first three courses on shallow broaches.
- The width of the hip shingles should be determined by the proportions of the whole spire. It is very important to get the hips in proportion with the spire.
- As the shingling approaches the top of the broaches, great care should be taken that a course will go over the broach without a noticeable step. Often it is not the same course for each broach.
- The importance of the level line becomes apparent. Unless the angle between the top of the broach and the facet is very steep, it always pays to put a lead flashing at this point. The broach and the half-hip should be finished with a half-course. The lead flashing should just cover this half-course, supported on lead or stainless steel clips, dressed up the spire 6" (150mm). The lead should be treated with grey bituminous paint as soon as the dressing is finished.
- Once a continuous course is around the spire, the level line should be abandoned and the courses taken up with a gauged axe. This stops the appearance becoming too uniform.
- The eight mitred corners to the octagonal spire should be closely mitred and laced together alternately every other course. There is no need for soakers to these mitred corners on octagonal spires, although we always fit stainless steel soakers to square on plan spires.

This work can now be safely carried out from bosun's chairs, all fitted with separate safety lines. The shingling can continue up until it becomes difficult to work from chairs – usually about the last ten feet of shingling. Where a square on plan platform can be erected using the bosun's chairs, this scaffold platform should be boarded and hand-railed and extended up with progress.

We use virtually the same specifications for oak, sweet chestnut or cedar shingles, with the courses and the boarding being the only difference. And of course we like to add a ventilator under the leadwork at the apex; there is usually enough air lower down coming in through the eaves and louvre openings.

Also when using cedar shingles we often like to stagger the butt line. This gives the appearance much more texture, but you need to bring the courses down to 4½" with no more than ¼" stagger. If the stagger is any greater it completely ruins the effect.

Chapter Fifteen

The Tops

The top of any wooden spire is often the cause of a lot of problems and also often the first indication that there is a problem. The first sign from the ground is when the finial moves out of upright. Usually somebody notices this, although by then it is often already too late.

You can almost divide the tops of timber spires into two categories, medieval and Victorian. On a typical medieval top the lead was nearly always very heavy gauge and bossed over the top of the crown post with the legs of the finial extending down approximately 18" with a ring driven down the legs with small catches holding the legs firmly against the lead-covered post, simple but efficient blacksmith work.

The Victorian tops were much more elaborate with very much heavier weathervanes, much bigger finials with a lot of scrolls and embellishments. Because of this extra weight and wind loading they extended the vane rod down through the lead and usually down as far as the first cruciform and ring beam, on some more elaborate spires they extended the vane rod down to wall plate level. But for all their fancy leadwork and massive timberwork, they never seemed to be able to seal the leadwork around the vane rod. I don't think for a moment that they started leaking immediately, but by the time they were on their second renewal of the covering, after approximately a hundred years, they had severe problems, but again because of massive timbers and excellent carpentry nobody noticed the movement and those that did totally ignored it.

It is amazing how many spires we have gone to ten or fifteen years after they had major works, including refurbishment of the weathervane and finial, where they have sealed gaps with car body filler, and a very few years later the weathervane and finial go seriously out of upright. This brings me back to my earlier remarks about architects not insisting that the contractors use men trained in church spire restoration.

Although the medieval top is not as attractive as some of the Victorian finials, with its very spindly vane rod and very basic leadwork, topped with a small flag or arrow, it has stood the test of time with many still there after several re-covers. So when we carry out major work to the apex of any timber spire we always try to talk the architects into converting the tops to this type of fixing. There is no problem getting the church to agree, as it makes good economic sense, but architects have often got different views and priorities.

The medieval type of finial fixing is widely known in the South of England as a "lantern fixing", the reason for this being that when the finial is not on the post the base looks rather like a lantern. There is little doubt that this is by far the best finial fixing for a timber spire, but it is not infallible. It relies on the accuracy of the measurements given to the blacksmith and the details of the clamp.

On one spire we worked on the architect specified that as

well as the clamp he wanted the legs drilled and screwed, completely defeating the purpose of not piercing the lead.

I never understand why contractors remove their scaffolding and rigging, which has cost the church a lot of money, and leave the job unfinished. Taking the money and running is not good enough. There have been occasions when other contractors have asked us, and no doubt others, for assistance or advice. One that comes to mind is a spire in Berkshire, it was a tall parapet spire covered with handmade clay tiles. The firm of steeplejacks that were doing the job, was a very well-known firm, who I believe carry out mostly industrial work to a very high standard.

They put two men on the job who laddered and erected a platform around the apex, a "flying deck" they called it. To put a flying deck on the top of a tiled spire is no mean feat, so good men! The job was to support the weathervane and finial ready for inspection. But for whatever reason they decided to dismantle the whole top. The top of the spire was a typical late Victorian, with the vane rod piercing the very over-decorated leadwork. Water had been penetrating the top of this spire for many years, so that the rafter tops and the crown post, including the lead-covered wooden boss, were all completely rotten. The two steeplejacks dismantled everything down to the flying deck, lowered it all to the ground and took the finial to the local blacksmith, but as he had no drawings or dimensions he couldn't do too much. The jacks covered the top of the spire and left.

Some days later the firm of steeplejacks doing the work contacted us. They had got our names from the National Federation of Master Steeplejacks. They asked us to rebuild the top using their scaffolding. So we rebuilt the top, did some sketches and delivered them to the blacksmith and completed the job. It's a pity that this job hadn't been thought through sooner; it would have saved the church a lot of money.

Another interesting top that we rebuilt was down in West Sussex. We had gone there to repair the oak shingles and, after laddering up and fixing a small platform near the top, we found that the finial was very loose, swaying from side to side in the wind. This was a strange top. There was no lead apron or capping – the whole top was cast iron. It seems that back on the mid-nineteenth century there was a foundry in this small town and as they made the iron cappings for factory chimneys, perhaps they thought they could design and produce a top for the spire on the church.

Some years earlier, perhaps early in the nineteenth century, this spire had been truncated and a very poor arrangement of timber and lead had been used to cap the spire. This had caused endless problems over the years as it is not easily accessed so they had a complete cap and apron cast locally. This now meant that the original finial could not be used again, so a new iron finial was made with added scrolls. They kept the original weathervane, which is a six foot long arrow, very primitive in its appearance, looking more as if it dated back to the dinosaurs.

When we arrived on the scene in the late 1960s the cap, apron and finial had been up there for nearly a century. No wonder it was all very loose. We told the church our finding. It was roughly what they expected and they asked us to go ahead with the work.

The first thing was to remove the arrow weathervane, a very heavy, very crude weathervane, but when we started to remove the finial we found it was fixed to the long vane rod, probably 15 feet in length. We didn't want to go to the bother of fixing up a headtree, so we stripped as much of the scrolls and other embellishments as possible and I was volunteered to lift it out. I stood astride on top of the iron cap and started to lift. As I lifted, the remains of the finial got higher and higher and became more and more top heavy. I know that I had worked on the circus some years before, but this was a balancing act with a difference. I eventually got to the end, lifted it out of the cap, watching the tip to keep the balance, and lifted it sideways, putting the end between two scaffold boards so that I could lower the rod down through the boards until it was low enough to tether to the handrail. With all that effort my poor old legs were shaking.

We still had to fix a headtree above, as the cast iron cap was so heavy we had to use a block and tackle to lift it. As we lifted the cap we were surprised to find it was full of honeycomb. Bees had been living inside for years. After we had lowered it down to the ground level we were asked to put the weathervane back up with a temporary steel cone to last until they could afford to do a complete re-cover a few years later. Some twenty years later we were back again, rebuilding the top and recovering the complete spire with cedar shingles.

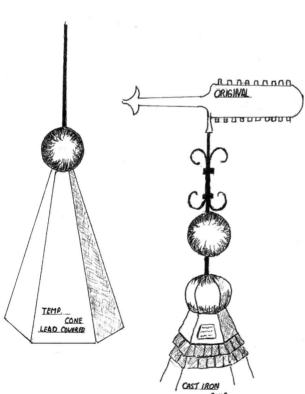

During the work we were often asked about the iron cap. It seemed that a lot of locals were disappointed that we were not going to replace it. They felt that it was one of the last surviving pieces of evidence of the old foundry. One of those locals turned out to be the curator of the local museum and he thought that we had scrapped it, but he was wrong as this cap was still standing in our yard where we had used it as a template to make the temporary cone that was still in place. As we were going to rebuild the top of the spire in timber, he had thought they might keep the temporary cap to show people in their museum, but as the iron cap was still available he was delighted and as far as I know it's still there today.

As we neared the end of this job, the architect told us about another church in Sussex which he looked after and the finial was out of upright, not badly but some of the parishioners had brought this to his attention and he thought that it would only take a day or so to put right. So could we have a look for him?

When we arrived at the church I was surprised just how big the spire was. I also agreed with the parishioners: it was quite badly out of upright.

We ran our ladders up to the lead capping and gave the finial a good shake. It was quite worrying because this top had only been restored about ten years before and looking at the leadwork I was having serious doubts about the whole job. I spoke to the architect and told him that we would need to erect scaffolding at the apex before opening up to see what the problem was. He was rather unhappy about this but told us to go ahead, so we erected our deck and opened up the spire.

It was unbelievable. I don't think I have ever seen such poor workmanship. There were bits of four-by-two jammed under the finial and the leadwork was wrapped around and nailed. No wonder the finial had moved – I was surprised that it had lasted that long. The most ridiculous thing was that on one of the lengths of four-by-two the men who carried out this work had written their names, proudly putting their age and dates. They had also written the name of the company they worked for. Obviously their supervisor and the architect hadn't bothered to look at the work.

We gave them a very reasonable price to rebuild this top. The church was horrified as they had spent large amounts of money only a few years ago and the parishioners could still remember the appeal for money and dipping their hands in their pockets. We made the weathervane safe and sealed the top, removed our ladders and drove away. I thought if we had charged them it would add insult to injury.

It was soon after his job was completed when I got a phone call. It was on a Sunday and we were just about to start lunch. It was from a well-known firm of steeplejacks who were working on the Houses of Parliament. They had been employed to gild the large iron crowns that adorn the four pinnacles on the Victoria Tower and they had run into some problems. They had a couple of young trainee steeplejacks who had never done any gilding and the engineer in charge compared the gilding on those crowns to the gilding on the royal coaches. He was extremely fussy and meticulous about the finished work. He was making life difficult for the contractors, which is why they had rung me, knowing that we had done a lot of gilding on weathervanes and clocks.

When we reached the platforms already around the pinnacles I was amazed at how much of these crowns had not been gilded before. The gilders who had carried out the gilding before obviously had not had tall scaffolds, so nobody inspected at close quarters. They had worked out just what parts could be seen from the ground and only gilded those, leaving the rest bare iron. Another example showing the need for inspection and insisting on trained workforce.

Chapter Sixteen

Restoration and Conservation

I believe that church steeplejacking, restoration and conservation should become one and the same, mainly because of the height and safety. When repairing a spire, be it wood or stone or any other material, you have to take in to account the fact that if the repair fails the chances are that it will fall. Restoration therefore becomes the priority; restoring rather than conserving, trying to keep the general appearance but with safety in mind.

Things started to go wrong during the war years, when the priority was just to make buildings safe no matter what the appearance was. The general idea was if it was or even looked unsafe: cut it off or take it down, with no thought of restoring it, not even at a later date. Lots of tops of spires were destroyed, with ironwork going to help the war effort, but as all of the iron railings and gates were being used to make weapons I suppose that was only fair. On some of the more important buildings, such as the Corn Exchange, the weathervanes were taken down and stored (as was Piccadilly's Eros) for the duration of the war. Others were protected, but there was no protection against bombs.

At the end of the war things slowly started to get repaired and I am sure that with the churches as with other buildings all work was done in order of priority and of course funding. By the early sixties and through the seventies, a lot of churches were being restored with major restoration projects. The Sussex and southern counties churches, which are of most interest to me, have a large percentage of wooden spires. Many were damaged by the war but also a lot just needed attention. You get a six year war which equates to about twenty years of no maintenance. Nobody was interested in the years leading up to the war and nobody was interested in the first few years after the conflict ended. But eventually church architects started to show their talent in restoration and work started.

They wanted to show their skills in bringing the churches back to their original condition, but also show they could use new materials and ideas to enhance the beautiful building which had been damaged. I think on a lot of churches they missed the mark. I feel that more time was spent thinking about new ideas than about restoring what we already had. Many of the church spires that had been truncated to make them safe during the war years and the beautiful weathervanes that had been safely hidden away, were not put back. The spires were capped and left with an inferior new or adapted weathervane and finial. This left a spire the modern architect was perhaps happy with, but not with the vision that the original architect intended and had achieved many years before.

We have worked on so many churches over the past years that have been truncated to different degrees. Perhaps it is only me, but as I travel around the country I always stop and like to look at the church from a distance, where the proportions should look right in the surroundings. I then go into the church where there is often an old painting or photograph of how it looked before some philistine had got to work with his saw.

One particular church in Surrey, where I was asked to repair the ageing shingles, is a rather special church that although very close to a town, is still untouched by modern development. It is surrounded by large mature trees and farm land. You can sit in your car or on the seat just inside the gate – very peaceful, and experience almost the same feeling and view locals must have known many years before. I say "almost" because when you look at the church as a whole you notice that the slender broached spire is out of proportion.

Sometime after the war the covering on the spire was changed from oak to cedar shingles and obviously the top had been leaking and the top of the crown post was rotten. The craftsmen who were carrying out the restoration, cut the post off down to solid timber, wrapped the original lead over the top and nailed it down, stuck the remains of the finial and the cockerel back on top and this is what we see today.

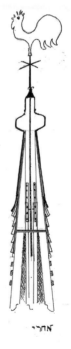

I brought this to the notice of the people that I was doing the repairs for, but heard no more. Several years later I was asked to go back there again as the woodpeckers had been busy and the shingles were now getting old and past their best. I did the repairs and again reported that the top was leaking. I prepared detailed drawings showing how it would look and how it could be extended back to its full height, but again heard nothing.

On another church, again in Surrey only in a different vein, we were asked to work on the restoration of a very early church which dated back to the eleventh century and I believe is mentioned in the Domesday Book.

This church has a crenelated tower with a lead and shingled dome roof topped with an iron finial and flag weathervane. We were asked to replace the whole roof covering with hand-cleft oak shingles and all the lead was to be recast. We were very pleased to get this contract as it was a very important restoration, on a very important building. However, there would be problems as at that time nobody was making oak shingles in any quantity and nobody was very interested in recasting the lead.

I spoke to the architect, who was very much into restoring ancient churches and agreed that we should make the shingles ourselves and recast as much of the old lead as was possible and make up the deficit with new cast lead. I spoke to her about the parapets, which were in red brick on a local sandstone tower. I thought – and still think – that this was a bit odd. I think that they stand out like a sore thumb. She explained that these parapets had only been built ten years before and the previous architect's thinking was that anyone who looked at them would know that they were not original. I could see the point but I am not sure that I agree with it.

We then bought some oak trees from a local timber man who was felling nearby and started making shingles – a long, laborious task, 10,000 shingles.

We set up a table, bought some casting sand and set about melting and recasting the lead using our table and a wooden strike. We had to melt some of it again, but in the end we produced some pretty good sheets.

When we had used all the lead, we got the rest from Norwich from the same people who had sold us the casting sand and given us very good advice on casting lead.

About the time that we were doing this job there was another job going on a church in West Sussex. This was a complete rebuild of the spire. This spire had only been reshingled with cedar shingles a few years previously, but had caught fire mysteriously one night. As there was no electricity in the tower or spire and nobody was working on the church, they blamed it on a bird dropping a lighted cigarette.

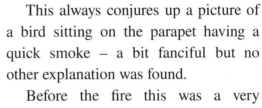

This always conjures up a picture of a bird sitting on the parapet having a quick smoke – a bit fanciful but no other explanation was found.

Before the fire this was a very elegant spire, tall and slender with a large oak finial cross, beautifully proportional and quite a landmark when driving towards Kent. Now it has been rebuilt and looks more like a post-war truncated spire. I accept that there has to be modern materials used but surely they should try and keep some sort of resemblance to the original concept.

It is possible to combine the two – modern materials and past appearances. A good example of this is another church in Sussex, towards Petworth, where the spire was blown down during the war and the church stood without a spire for a number of years until the late 50s, early 60s. It was rebuilt using a steel frame with timber rafters bolted to the frame, boarded, and then covered with cedar shingles. There were no oak shingles available at the time, but in this case the architect who designed the new spire managed to keep an appearance acceptable to the conservationist-minded but nobody who has any interest in churches would think it was original. In my opinion this is the type of repair that shows the thought and compromise that should satisfy most people.

A very good example of new work merging into older work is on a church in south London, famous because it is claimed that Turner often sat there and painted some of his river scenes. It is a fine brick building with Portland stone features. The church tower is of brick and the lantern with the three clock dials is timber with copper cladding. The timber spire above is a hardwood frame with softwood boarding but this spire was covered with large sheet copper all with flattened single welts.

At some time after the war years the clock area and lanterns were re-coppered with much smaller sheets. The cornices above the clocks were also recovered with copper at the same time, but although the copper sheeting on the spire must have been suspect, it was decided to leave alone, probably because of finance. Sheet copper done traditionally is very expensive. Unfortunately some twenty-five to thirty years later the large sheets of copper started to come loose and become dangerous. We were asked to do temporary repairs and make safe. When we got up to the spire it was not only the copper that was loose. On the boarding that the copper was fixed to, the old handmade nails had rusted completely making it a very dangerous building. We did all that we could to make it safe and reported the bad news to the vicar.

A few weeks later we were invited to a meeting at the church where the problems would be discussed. The inspecting architect, the vicar, churchwardens and contractors, including ourselves, were present. The first thing that was discussed was: how long will it stay safe? I thought a couple of months at the most, other contractors thought less, but we all agreed that the wheels should be set in motion immediately. The next thing was: how much would it cost? Nobody expected firm figures, but they really needed to start planning and get faculties and permissions etc. Then they needed to know what method we all intended to use. The other contractors plumped for a full scaffold, sheeted in with a temporary roof. I suggested that we erect a fan scaffold from above the lantern arches, then use bosun's chairs up to the top ten feet, where we would put fully boarded scaffolding extended up to the weathervane.

Everyone except the vicar and churchwardens almost had a coronary. They heatedly argued that it had never been done that way before and they knew it would not work. I argued that because they had never done it this way, didn't mean that it could not be done. When you consider the saving, it should be considered, and as our method complied with all the regulations, I could not see there was a valid argument against it.

After the architect had prepared the tender forms, the three companies were asked to tender and submit their method statements. One of these was ours and to the surprise of everyone we were asked to do the job. They had doubts about our methods but it seemed that money was short and ours was by far the cheapest option.

In due course we started by erecting a platform around the base of the spire. This was a cross between a working scaffold and a protective fan. From this platform we could strip off the first six feet of copper sheeting and the softwood boarding. It had already been decided to replace all the boarding, as it was too thin and in poor condition. We cleaned the rafters and re-boarded, then fixed the first row of copper sheets. Up to this point we were working with conventional methods but once we had sheeted up as far as we could comfortably reach, we started using bosun's chairs. We could strip and re-board the next section quite easily and fix temporary covers.

We were now ready to start sheeting out of bosun's chairs. This is where some people expected things to go wrong. We had a chap working with us who had done some sheet metal work before, so he came up with his tape measure and notebook and with our help measured a row of sheets recording the dimensions on his note pad. Then he went back to his bench set up in the lantern and with a mate folded and formed the row of sheets. He formed half a row of sheets which we fixed while he folded and formed the next half of a row. This kept everyone fully employed and the job progressing steadily. We continued like this until we had reached approximately 15 feet from the apex, where we fixed a cropper-held deck, sometimes referred to as a Yankee deck, from which we extended up with traditional scaffolding to the apex.

It was a well-executed and safely carried out job despite everyone's doubts. No doubt the purists will say that the welts should have been flattened and not standing seams, and that we should not have changed the sheet sizes, but I think it was a good compromise with the conservator and the Copper Development Association both reasonably happy.

With both lead and copper it is possible to keep a similar pattern as the original and comply with modern regulations, but when it comes to stone repairs it is quite a different story as using a different or better stone can stand out like a sore thumb. I remember a huge church on the Sussex coast that we had surveyed. Over the years there had been a number of plastic stone repairs which were beginning to fail. We were asked by the Cathedral Works Organisation to take out the plastic repairs and piece in natural stone.

As our ladders were already fixed up the spire we were asked to start immediately. We only got the job because this was a large spire and would have cost an awful lot of money to scaffold. We started by erecting a fan scaffolding around the base of the spire. This was mainly to protect people and roofs below. Then we started chopping out all the plastic stone repairs that we could reach from this platform while waiting for the new stone to be delivered. Because nobody knew exactly how much stone would be needed, they sent us a complete quarry stone, about five tons that had been cut into two inch scants, leaving us to cut whatever sizes we needed.

But before we could start cutting, English Heritage sent an architect to check on exactly what we were doing. They looked at the areas we had cut out and were happy. They even complimented us on how well we had cut out the plastic stone repairs, but they were not at all happy with the choice of stone. The Cathedral Works had sent us a whole quarry stone, cut into two inch scants, of St Maxime, a French stone and a very good match for Bath stone but without any flaws. It is a very pure stone that when tapped with a hammer rings like a bell. English Heritage thought that the purists might want Bath stone, but eventually – because, when weathered, St Maxine looks more like Bath stone than Bath stone – they said that we could go ahead with the stone repairs.

We started cutting out all the old plastic repairs and also areas that had deteriorated since the last repairs and as we progressed it was good to see just how well this stone matched the original. We spent the next three months chopping out and piecing in new stone. The higher we got the more stone needed to be replaced, but eventually we reached the top spire lights where we sealed up the openings leaving just enough for trickle ventilation. We then had to erect a scaffolding just above the spire lights to give access to the capstone and finial. The cap was a dome-shaped stone which was badly eroded. We cut the top half off completely and pieced in a new stone. It was a pleasure to work the shape to match the original because St Maxine is flawless, whereas in Bath stone you get veins of quartz, sea shells and soft pockets, making it much harder to keep the shape.

The finial was rather a flimsy wrought iron vane rod with very sparse embellishments. There was no weathervane. I don't think there ever was. When this spire was built in 1872 there was an artist's impression in the London News, showing the church and spire with a very tall, beautifully proportioned finial and a large cockerel weathervane. It was a point of discussion when about thirty-five years later the architect wanted to restore the top of the spire to its original condition in his view. He insisted that there had been a finial and weathervane, exactly as in the artist's impression, and wanted it reinstated. I can reassure whoever reads this that there never was a weather cockerel and that the iron finial was original. Passing the church now if you look up you will see that there is a gilded cockerel and small finial, very nicely done but nowhere near as gracefully proportioned as the artist's impression. This is typical of the type of argument you get with restoration and conservation work: the architect and craftsman never agree and the architect usually wins.

Another good point on this church are the massive oak louvre blades. On the south and west elevations they were in very poor condition and had to be removed. English Heritage wanted them replaced in English oak but the church and the Cathedral Works wanted to use much cheaper and easily obtained iroko, an African hardwood. Eventually it was decided to go for the cheaper version and today, some forty years later, it is hard to tell the difference-- a very good example of using different materials in older buildings. When given enough thought you can still keep the appearance without hiding the fact that it is not original.

While writing and thinking about this large Sussex spire it brought back memories of the time when we laddered this spire many years ago to do an inspection of the stonework and weathervane. When I arrived with my equipment and started laddering up the west wall of the tower, several people stopped to watch. They seemed fascinated that it was possible to fix ladders to a sheer wall on my own. Most of us at some time have laddered on our own. It is not a problem just very hard work. To ladder up the inside was a different problem, as there were several floors to this tower plus the belfry and ringing chamber, so I needed help to pass the ladders and other equipment up through the floors. As my own men were busy elsewhere, I took a young man on. He told me that he had done this sort of work before and was frightened of nothing. So we started passing the equipment up through the trap doors to the lower rooms of the tower. We got the equipment up as far as the ringing chamber then stopped for lunch. We had brought sandwiches and flasks with us, so we had our lunch sitting in the ringing chamber talking about our previous jobs and where we had travelled. He had been everywhere and done almost everything. After lunch we needed to get the equipment up through the silence chamber and through the belfry to the base of the spire.

There was a stout wooden ladder leading up from the ringing chamber to a trap door in the ceiling that looked very heavy, so I sent the new fellow up to open it and put the light on. Usually with this sort of trapdoor when you lift the trapdoor and put your hand in and feel around, you can find the switch. My new mate lifted the door and was groping around for the switch when he suddenly pulled his hand out, let the door drop and jumped off the ladder, landing in a heap on the ringing chamber floor. He looked terrified and was shaking. After he calmed down I asked him what the matter was. He explained that he was terrified of all reptiles, to the point that if he saw one he would often pass out. He said that when he was feeling for the switch he had felt the skin of a reptile.

When I asked him what type of reptile he had found, he said he thought it was a crocodile. I was surprised, as you don't find many crocodiles inside church towers. In fact, you don't find many crocodiles *outside* church towers. But he insisted that there was a crocodile in the silence chamber. So I climbed the ladder and opened the door very carefully, peering through the crack and looking for the light switch.

I eventually found the light switch and turned it on, half expecting to hear something. I'm not sure what I expected, as I don't know what noise a crocodile makes. But as I heard nothing I opened the door a little wider and then I saw it. It was a crocodile – ! – albeit a very small one, and it was dead and stuffed. I really should not have been surprised as the silence chamber does no more than deaden the noise for the ringers below and is often used as a store for unwanted material waiting for the next jumble sale etc.

After I had removed the offending creature we got on with the job of laddering the inside of the spire.

This turned out to be quite a big job and we were there for several weeks. The celebrated reptile hunter left us soon after the incident with the croc and my own men joined me on this job. We had our caravans in the car park at the rear of the church as we were staying on site, and sometimes at lunch time we would go to the local Wimpy café to save cooking at night. On one occasion somebody suggested that we should take the crocodile with us, as we had told one of the waitresses about it and she said she would like to meet it.

So a few days later we went to lunch carrying the crocodile wrapped up in a coat. Once inside and sitting down with the crocodile under the table we waited for the waitress to come over. A different waitress came over and told us that the other girl was off for the day. Not wanting to take the croc back, someone came up with the idea of putting it in the ladies' toilet. The toilets in there were very long and narrow, more like narrow passages with the toilet right at the end. We put the croc in a sitting position beside the toilet with its mouth open, looking as if it was smiling, and left it.

We were eating our lunch and began wondering if any ladies were ever going to use the toilet before we had to go back to work. Then suddenly this huge woman came in with her husband. She was enormous, one of our lads referred to her as "the eighteen wheeler". She told her husband to "Sit!" and after a while she went to the toilet. We could hardly believe our luck. As I have already said, these are very long narrow toilets, so we imagined that she would have to shut the door and back up to the toilet. We waited what seemed a long time, then we heard it! A long scream followed by a crashing sound. That's when we left the café and went back to work.

There is so much criticism about using different materials on ancient buildings, but sometimes the doubters and the critics should look back at some of the falsehoods in building and conservation. A couple of years ago, I was invited to a seminar at the Weald and Downland Museum at Singleton. The title of the seminar was Falsehoods in Building. The first session was tuck-pointing, where restorers had tried to make much older brickwork look very smart. The best known example of this is numbers 10 and 11 Downing Street, W1, but there are many more buildings which now boast this restoration.

The next session was about Coade stone, of which there are so many sites, a really marvellous man-made stone. I am doing

Eleanor Coade an injustice saying "man-made", perhaps "artificial stone" is better. This stone was used on so many important buildings, including royal buildings, but a few still think it is un-conservational. Another falsehood not mentioned at that seminar was mathematical tiles. These are tiles that look like bricks and many ancient buildings are clad with these. So although I am all for restoring and conserving our ancient buildings, sometimes there has to be compromise.

During the 1960s, '70s and '80s, plastic repairs were very much to the fore. You could see stonemasons walking around sites with armfuls of Cementone containers mixing up their plastic stone, usually a mixture of white cement, some lime, several types of aggregates and a little crushed stone or dust, and of course the Cementone. These masons were often referred to as Hank, Clint or Hoppy, some well-known cowboy names, but not often to their faces. But for all these jokes, well-executed plastic stone repairs really did stand the test of time and on many churches today if you look carefully there are good repairs fifty-odd years later. But the emphasis is on "look carefully" or you will miss it, it blends in so well. But nothing beats a good natural stone repair and in many cases there is little difference in the cost.

Chapter Seventeen

The Laurie Young Method

Earlier I described how we erect our ladders and other equipment, which is what I believe to be the general practice among steeplejacks. But I will always read any publication that I think might be relevant to our work (never too old to learn).

Some years ago I bought Clifford W. Ashley's classic *The Ashley Book of Knots*, which is reputed to be the Holy Grail on the subject. No doubt this is the most comprehensive book on knots and bends together with associated uses of rope. There are many chapters about how to reeve a block and tackle, and safety ropes, bosun's chairs etc., but there is also a chapter about steeplejacking.

He gleaned information from Laurie Young, a well-known steeplejack from eastern Massachusetts whose text and sketches are unbelievable and I believe, most of them impossible. His method of climbing a spire was you climbed out of the top of the louvered openings; ideally these openings should be at the base of the spire. From these openings you pass a rope around the spire, flick the rope up as far as you can reach and tie as tightly as possible. From this rope you hang a bosun's chair with a hook attached to it. You then climb into this chair. Then you stand on the chair seat and flick another rope around the spire, reaching up as high as possible, tighten this rope and hang another bosun's chair from this rope, climb up into the upper chair ready to repeat the whole operation again.

I believe this method is impossible. The average village church spire is about 80 to 100 feet around the base. It would take a very good and clever man to flick a rope up and tie it.

Another technique of his was the "one hitch", which was his method of getting down again. After you had finished your work – which I hope didn't take long, sitting up there waiting for the paint to dry and then second coating it – you would need to remove all the ropes etc., drop those to the ground.

How you do this without them getting caught up, he never explained. You then rig your "one hitch", which consists of a loop of rope wrapped around the spire until the two loops meet you then pass your chair rope through both loops, rig your chair and you are ready to lower yourself down and pull the rope out once you have reached the ground, shaking the loop of rope loose and it will fall. If any of this fails, i.e. some of the ropes get caught up or the loop doesn't fall, you get a steeplejack from England to ladder the spire for you and do the job.

His methods for working on flag staffs are possible but highly impractical. However, in fairness to him, his views and methods were published a long time ago and although they have been reprinted several times since, the ideas are still from way back.

Chapter Eighteen

Stories from Other Jacks

After reading about Laurie Young I started thinking about stories that other jacks had told me over the years. One was the story told by a steeplejack that had worked for me for several years. His father had told him the story and he asked for my opinion.

His father claimed that soon after the war was over he and several others were dismantling some very large wooden pylons. It seemed that a lot of these had been built during the war years for communication. I can personally remember two of these enormous structures situated at Hindhead in Surrey where, standing on top of the hill by the Devil's Punch Bowl, they must have commanded a fantastic view over the surrounding countryside, the ideal spot for a radio mast.

The pylons his father was referring to were somewhere in the north of England. He claimed they were eight hundred feet high (like most unverified stories, probably exaggerated). He claimed they were working by just standing on the timbers and as they were lowering a very large crosspiece that was wet and slimy with algae it slipped, trapping one of the men's arms. He said there was no point in calling the emergency services as he doubted they could have reached the injured man. They decided to cut the timber to try to free the man's arm. This would be very painful, but they had no first aid boxes in those days, just some old pieces of rag for him to bite on.

They cut the timber, ignoring the poor man's screams, and after about an hour they got his arm out. But it was obvious that it was badly broken and there was no chance of him being able to climb down. By this time the man was barely conscious. So the storyteller sent a young labourer down to get a large backpack from his van. He didn't tell anyone what was in the bag: "Just bring it all up!" While waiting for the lad to get back up, which would take some time (a long, dangerous climb with a rucksack), the men made the injured man comfortable and tied him up so he could not move and fall. Then they all moved over to the other side of the pylon and had a cup of tea while they waited. The injured man was barely conscious and past caring.

The storyteller then explained his plan. After he had left the army, where he had served with Special Forces, he had just taken up a new and dangerous sport called base jumping. Nutty thrill-seekers jump off buildings with just a parachute, throwing a drogue as they jump to open the main parachute, and by using the lift webs, steer it away from the building. One of the men pointed out that the injured man would not be able to move, so could not steer the chute at all. The storyteller said that as long as they threw the man out far enough, and downwind, he should miss the pylon. He also said that he had told the lad who had gone down to get the equipment to ring the emergency services (no mobiles in those days) so they would be waiting at the base.

They wrapped the injured man in a tarpaulin and tied him

up so that he could not move, but they didn't tell him of the plan as they thought it might worry him. He had livened up a bit, so they gave him a smoke while they waited. Eventually the lad appeared, puffing and blowing, with the huge rucksack and they started rigging up the equipment. The injured man started to get excited and was screaming and swearing and saying he would take his chances climbing down, but of course he couldn't. He was tied up. So the storyteller and one other got hold of each end of the injured man and, standing as near the edge as possible, swung him back and forward to get enough of a swing and on the third swing they let him go as another man threw the drogue. Then they watched as the chute opened and he drifted down to the waiting ambulance and landed with a very hard, painful bump. The storyteller went down to explain to the authorities exactly what had happened and to retrieve and pack his parachute ready for the next time. Base jumping is still practised today but parachutes are very different and far easier to control, but I don't think our friends in Health and Safety would recommend this as a safe method of rescue.

At around this time we were working in the West End. I think we were working on All Souls, just off Regent Street, when I heard some of my friends were erecting a large scaffolding on County Hall near Westminster Bridge. I was interested as I had been involved in work on the many chimneys some time before. They were building a temporary roof over part of the building and were playing some games. It has always been this way in this trade or craft. They had a rope and ginny wheel rigged up to pull the corrugated iron sheets and, as it was lunch time and they were probably fed up with the boring job of fixing them, they were playing.

In those days it was normal practice to challenge your mates to a contest. In this case it was who could pull themselves up the farthest on the rope and wheel. They had tied a loop in one end of the rope which you sat in and pulled the other end, lifting yourself off the ground and whoever got the highest was the winner--very simple. But as these were young strong men and the scaffolding was only about 100 feet high it didn't really test them. They told me about an Irishman who had challenged them. He had devised a task that would really challenge them to the limit. The idea was that you tied a bowline in the rope (a fixed loop, for those not familiar with the bowline), which you then place around your neck then pull the other rope and up you go. Nobody accepted the challenge. The Irishman then asked for bets as to how far he could pull himself up. He claimed it was easy if you didn't try to breathe.

A few of the men bet him a breakfast or a couple of pints. There was no way he could back down; the pride of the Irish nation was on the line here. He slipped the noose over his head and adjusted it so that the rope pulled up from the back. He explained that if you pulled it up from the side like the hangman did, it would break your neck. Then he removed his cap, rolled it up and stuffed in the noose at the front under his chin and he was then ready to go.

Everyone stood back to give him plenty of room and he took a mighty breath of air and started pulling. He climbed fairly quickly for a few feet then started slowing down. One of the other men had the presence of mind to hold on to the end of the rope that Patrick was pulling. Suddenly he stopped pulling and looked as if he was about to let go. The man holding the rope suddenly had all the weight, because Patrick had passed out. They quickly lowered him down, stretched him out on the ground and he started to come round. It seemed that although he could hold his breath long enough, the rope had cut off the supply of blood to his brain, causing him to black out. All bets were off.

After they had told me this story and they had finished their games with the rope and wheel, we sat and talked for a bit, laughing about Patrick and his antics. I then told them about a man who could pull himself up about 100 feet on a rope and wheel with one arm tied behind his back. They thought this was quite a feat, but in theory it should be possible and they wanted to try it. The rope and wheel was there and a few of the men, so why not? Again they started challenging each other with bets of breakfast or pints and several of them tried it, but nobody got very far. They were laughing and joking, taking the mickey out of each other, when I told them that I could do it with ease.

Some of these men were extremely strong and fit and I was never a Mr Muscles, so they challenged me. I told them that I would alter the rigging of the rope and wheel but I would still leave it a single whip exactly as they had tried. They agreed that as long as I left it single whip they didn't care what I did, because if they couldn't do it, neither could I. Well, I did it, twice, with the greatest of ease, but I did cheat and no bets were won. We all had a great laugh and a long lunch break.

Another story that I was told, it was about third or fourth hand by the time I got to hear it. It was about this jack who was going on a camping holiday with his family, but they had his mother living with them. She was very old and frail and they had nobody to look after her, so they decided to take her with them. They hired a separate tent so they got some privacy. They thought going to the Continent would be nice and warm for her. They drove to Dover and caught the ferry to France. Everything seemed fine. They drove down to the South of France, stopping and camping at regular intervals, then were going to stay on that site for a week before returning.

They had only been there a couple of days when Granny died in her sleep. They weren't sure what to do. They were worried about the local authorities as they could be difficult about these things and they didn't want any delays, so they wrapped Granny up in a tarpaulin and tied her on the roof rack. They decided to leave early and head straight back home, hoping for an earlier ferry. They left the camping site, making some excuse or other, said goodbye to all their new friends and set off. After several hours on the road they pulled in to a café for a meal and a break. After the meal they were ready to head on towards the ferry. They got out to the car park only to find, to their horror, that the car had been stolen – including Granny. According to the storyteller they never saw the car or Granny again.

I would have loved to see the thieves' faces when they opened up the tarpaulin-wrapped parcel on the roof. It all sounds a little far-fetched to me, but still a good story.

Another story told to me by another steeplejack was about two steeplejacks who were asked to paint a couple of downpipes on a church tower in Kent. It was a tall ragstone tower with a crenelated parapet. The two downpipes were situated on the north and south faces of the tower and were opposite each other diagonally across the tower, one on the north-east corner and one on the south-west corner. There were no obvious fixings for bosun's chairs, so they decided to put a wire rope across the tower and fix their chair blocks to each end. After getting the paint and brushes etc. in a couple of buckets hung over the sides, the two jacks climbed up onto the parapets, getting into their chairs and hanging onto the parapet at a given signal (a shout!) they lowered their weight into the chairs. Looking through the crenelations they could just see other and signalled that everything was okay.

They started work cleaning and painting the hoppers and downpipes. Everything was fine to start with. They could shout and hear each other, but as they got lower it was much harder to hear and understand what each other was saying. I don't think they realised just how bad these pipes were and how long the job would take. After a couple of hours one decided he needed to visit the toilet and was regretting the boozy night and strong curry he had enjoyed the night before. He sat there painting as fast as he could, trying to think about anything else– anything but toilets.

About ten feet from the ground, with at least another hour's painting to do, he had reached the point when you have to go. So he shouted to his mate, who shouted back, but neither really heard or understood what the other one said. He then lowered his chair and jumped out and ran on his tippy-toes to the bushes. When he returned his chair was halfway back up the downpipe. He ran round to the other side to find his mate sitting on a gravestone smothered in paint and very unhappy, but with only his pride damaged.

Chapter Nineteen

The Future of Steeplejacking

The future of steeplejacking as I see it rests firmly in the hands of the architects. It seems to me that many architects not only want the biggest and most expensive job but also never consider the best value for money as important. Every diocese has an advisory committee, where architects and the clergy sit side by side, listening to the problems from the parishes. They are extremely good at the administration and assisting with fundraising ideas, and in most cases they write a very good specification, particularly as far as the materials and mortar mixes etc., but when it comes to the method side so many seem lost.

Every job should comply with all regulations in force at the time, and should be interpreted to comply with these, but it seems to me that so many – and it's getting more and more – interpret the regulations to suit their own preferences, not always giving the church the best value for money. Some of the blame must be aimed at the clergy that sit on these committees. In my experience they never question the architects, no matter what the argument. I feel that if steeplejacking or roped access is going to continue saving money and helping with restoration of our churches in the future, there needs to be a committee set up within the church, formed by architects, engineers and access experts, who would not look for the most expensive method but the safest, most practical method of carrying out the work.

A fine example of mismanagement of the access was a church in Hampshire, where the tower and spire were to be reshingled, together with some timber repairs and replacements. The architects were very well known in church repair and restoration, and they had prepared an excellent specification taking in all the problems for the repairs. There was a site meeting pre-starting where the usual items were sorted out, i.e. toilets, parking, huts etc. Also on the agenda was access. I was asked to go along with the main contractor as an adviser. The architects also invited me along to advise on the shingling. One of them had attended one of my courses on church spire shingling at the Downland Museum, so it was a very friendly and successful meeting.

We – the main contractor and I – suggested that we erect a scaffolding to the west gable, extended up to the tower embracing the tower bearing on the arcading. We intended to use lightweight scaffolding, where we would get the required loading per square metre, I think it was about $2kN/m^2$. We submitted drawings and loadings for the work and the loading on the building, but the architects decided that there should be no loading on the building at all. In fact, they didn't want the scaffold to touch the building anywhere. They called in a scaffolding company to design a freestanding scaffold, completely covered in with a roof on top.

There were many problems as this scaffolding was being erected, causing long delays. There were so many arguments that by the time it was about half way up, when the job had to be stopped because it was so heavy, that where the base was started there were so many old graves, it started to sink, putting an enormous load on the building. This brought another problem, as there were bats living in the tower and spire. There was only a short window when the spire had to be completely stripped. If this could not be achieved the bat protection people would stop the job for several months.

I spoke at the emergency meeting and told them that had they listened to our advice the spire would have been completely stripped by now and probably half reshingled. They explained to the churchwardens that they decided there should be no weight on the building (very important). I calculated the weight on the building to be seven tons with the scaffolding still sinking; this was about five tons above the weight of the scaffolding we had suggested. We were then faced with the problem of getting the spire stripped before the bat window closed. The bat people made it very obvious that they had the last word and the site would be closed.

I suggested to the meeting that we could strip the spire and fix temporary covers to keep it waterproof, by using our steeplejacks' methods. The architects said that this was not allowed anymore and it was illegal. By this time I was getting fed up with hearing these lame excuses and told them that it was not illegal at all. I also explained to them that at the same time as this job was beginning to get very expensive, as all the equipment was on hire, including the unfinished scaffolding, and also there was an awful weight on the building they had said was unacceptable, but as they seemed to think that to strip the spire by using steeplejacks' methods was illegal I had to use the Shard as an example. Everyone in the building trade knows that the London Building Control is extremely strict and makes everyone obey the rules to the letter, so I pointed out that the Shard was being built 1,000 feet above the busy streets of London without any external scaffolding and only using roped access. This seemed to satisfy them and they agreed to let us strip the spire using our methods. It also satisfied the bat protection people.

The scaffolding people returned to the site and after altering their original design carried on, but they did not keep the weight off the building and ended up with about four to five tons on the arcading, far more than we had wanted to put on it. A very expensive job that cost the church tens of thousands of unnecessary expense. (Will people ever listen?)

I also think that the architects should always be able to safely inspect the work at any time during the contract, which is why we always erect towers or caged-in ladders, with all scaffolds boarded and hand-railed, to any areas where the architect wishes to inspect. One architectural practice from East Sussex that we had worked for many times got over this problem by sharing the problem. It was a small practice with just a couple of architects. One, whom I believe was the senior partner, didn't like heights at all and was not happy even on the first lift. It makes you wonder why he decided to work on churches, as quite a few have towers and spires. He was not that happy even inside the tower, when we sometimes had to lift the floorboard and he would always try to peer from the other side of the room. So if an inspection of the work was necessary he would always send out his partner, who was the complete opposite when it came to heights. But they always had plenty of work so their system must have worked well for them.

If steeplejacking on churches is going to have a future then firms, either steeplejacks or roped access, need to start training men and women in conservation and restoration techniques. The roped access people seem to train their employees in rope and climbing techniques, but work by using a tick list when carrying out surveys. This might work well on large concrete buildings and chimneys, and nobody every doubts their climbing abilities and their detail to safety, but they probably need more tuition in conservation. The steeplejacks certainly need more training in conservation, plus perhaps more training in climbing and rope technique.

It seems to me that a large percentage of contractors agree with the architects, no matter what the cost to the church. Nobody sees giving value for money as important. I recently went to a meeting at a church. I was only an adviser. I thought that the contractor could have reduced his price by several thousand pounds, as they were interested in our steeplejacks' methods, and to scaffold this building the conventional way was ridiculously expensive. The contractor didn't reduce his price enough; needless to say, the contract went elsewhere.

As well as the contractors, the architects and specifiers need to change their attitude towards church repairing. Perhaps when carrying out their quinquennial reports every five years they should think about the old saying: "A stitch in time…" I have always tried to persuade architects that on every third quinquennial report they should recommend that the spires or upper parts of the building should be inspected by trained steeplejacks, then small repairs carried out using steeplejack techniques might delay those repairs turning into bigger jobs needing expensive scaffolding.

Another strong point I am always trying to make is the use of permanent fixings. This is a point of discussion I have had with many an architect and many churchwardens over the years. I suggest that whenever they use a steeplejack they should insist that they put permanent fixings. These are usually just small rings of stainless steel, which are hardly visible from the ground but will make it much easier to fix ladders and much safer, and should make inspections and future work much cheaper.

As always there is someone who will put up an argument. I was at a meeting towards the end of a very large conservation contract, where I recommended that before the scaffolding came down it might be prudent to fix stainless steel permanent fixing to the spire and tower. The architect who had been overseeing the contract thought this was a very bad idea. He had obviously never tried laddering up or down in strong wind!

His objection was that the church would be liable if there was an accident while fixing or removing the ladders. I told him that the church should make it clear when accepting the quote for an inspection that the steeplejack should be responsible for inspecting the fixings and fully insured under their own policy. This has to go down as one of the most stupid arguments ever. I can understand why so many people are averse to having permanent fixing. It means that men with much less training could do the job. But as I have said at so many meetings and written in so many reports, the architects should insist and ensure that any firm who tenders for the work has men trained in church repairing steeplejacking!

Today everybody has different ideas. A short while ago architects and engineers started to use aerial platforms-- Simon hoists and cherry pickers, as they liked to call them. Then they started to hire lighter-than-air gas-filled balloons with cameras fitted to them. We were asked to use these on Guildford Cathedral with very poor results. These aerial cameras were okay for taking a view of the buildings and a panoramic view of the surrounding countryside, but were very limited when it came to a detailed examination of the condition of the fabric. They couldn't get detailed measurements and they couldn't always get around the back.

Lately everyone is saying that the best modern way is to use the dreaded drone, hated by pilots and lovers in the long grass. But again they're very limited; they can't get too close to the buildings and they can't measure. There is no doubt that, used by qualified pilots, they have their uses, but they are no substitute for a hands on inspection.

In my opinion there is no better way that a trained man close up to the building with a camera or a notebook and a tape measure in a bosun's chair to get a detailed report. I also think this is the cheapest way.

When we think about the future of our ancient timber spires we automatically think that the greatest danger to them is mainly the woodpeckers. I think the real danger to the integrity of these structures is not from the woodpeckers or the lack of maintenance but from the tele-communication people. A lot of 15th and 16th century spires that have survived all these years are a prime target for the telephone companies. They stand tall and proud above most of the surrounding buildings and forests. They are usually hollow except for the supporting timbers with bells in most of them being hung in the tower and rung from below leaving a large, almost empty space, high above the ground – the ideal spot to put a tele-communications mast. When approached, the church can't believe its luck – large sums of money with ongoing rent, an answer to their prayers. An awful lot of churches have thanked the Lord and taken the money.

I am not personally against the church allowing this equipment to be fitted in their towers and spires and I certainly agree with them taking the money. Much of this promised wealth is earmarked for repairs to the building but in some cases those repairs are caused by the fitting of the masts and other equipment, leaving the church no better off financially. I realise that most of this equipment is fitted by experts in their field but little thought goes into the conservation of the building. Therefore ancient timbers get removed and replaced with a piece of modern stainless steel or more often a piece of cheaper galvanised steel. This might do the job but the piece of ancient timber ends up in a wood burner, with all its carpenters' marks and dates lost forever.

I have seen a couple of examples where the mast fixers have knocked out old tree nails and replaced them with galvanised bolts, nodding and smirking that that's a much better job! Not once did they examine the old hand cleft tree nails for dates etc. It is well known that some of the old church builders often used to put a date or their initials on the centre of the nails where nothing would destroy it.

I was recently involved with a large timber spire of the late Victorian period. This is a tall spire constructed from pitch pine framing, soft wood boarding and originally covered with hand cleft oak shingles. It has since being re-covered with sawn cedar shingles. It is a beautifully proportioned spire with four very large lucarnes and four much smaller spire lights near the apex. It was agreed the telecommunications equipment would be put behind the lucarnes but the lucarnes needed some alternation. This was all carried out from inside the spire which meant there was a lot of lead hanging on the outside. This caused a problem when some pieces fell and other pieces were hanging loose, flapping in the wind. Eventually, the church called us in and a protective platform was erected around the tower and temporary repairs were carried out, at the church's cost.

The point here is that had the telecommunications people had training in conservation, or had they called in people to work on the outside of the building, it would have saved the church a lot of money and the building would look a lot better. I think this is a good example of where training and understanding the nature of the building together with some compromise and dialogue between the parties would save money and the building.

Driving around the country you see many examples of so called 'disguised' masts, some that are supposed to look like trees and some very fat flagstaffs. In my opinion a mast would look better because every time I see a tree that sticks out you just know it's a telecommunications mast. I think that there is a lot of scope to put communications equipment in church spires or towers but whoever controls it needs to discuss it with keen and knowledgeable conservationists.

Another spire that comes to mind is a small fletch originally built from oak and covered with sand cast lead but through lack of proper maintenance had got to the point of being dangerous. It was decided to dismantle the complete structure and using parts of the original gargoyles and other features as moulds reconstruct the whole thing from fibre glass. They erected a slim steel pylon out of the roof some 50ft above the roofline to which they attached the glass fibre panels to. As there was only one bell they hauled it up until it filled the metal pylon. This left the maximum amount of room in the lower parts of the pylon. I am sure that this was the intention of those forward-thinking designers. This was early days for telecommunications but there were problems. It would have been nice to be able to access the top part of the pylon but the bell filled the space.

A very short time after the whole fletch had been rebuilt, problems started to show up. The joints to the glass fibre panels had begun to leak. They engaged contractors to apply mastic pointing to all the joints outside which seemed to work for a few months. Then it started to leak again. This time we were asked to look at the problem. All the joints had been filled with mastic, if anything they had been over-filled giving the joints quite a clumsy appearance. I could understand the contractors thinking a bit of (belt and braces) but with the movement of the internal pylon and the thermal movement a lot of the joints had opened up again.

We refilled the open joints and contacted a firm that specialises in liquid plastics. They recommended a liquid plastic that came in dark grey that could be applied with a brush. We applied two coats of this plastic and heard no more but I am sure this will need to be recoated every few years. I think with the advantage of hindsight it would have been better and probably cheaper to have rebuilt this fletch using traditional materials and methods and there would still have been more room to fit the telecommunications equipment.

Walking through London a few weeks ago I paused and watched the men working erecting the scaffolding around the tower of Big Ben. There have been a lot of comments lately about the work going on there, mostly because they have to stop the clock striking, and about the cost and the amount of time that the clock will be silent.

In this country we have some of the finest scaffold systems in the world and also some of the finest scaffolders and riggers. You only need to walk around the city and look up at the construction work that is going on and see how thought and financial considerations have affected the design of the accesses. You realise that how much money and time can be saved.

I have had no involvement with the work to the Queen Elizabeth Tower, as it is now called, so I am not criticising how the work is being carried out. But I wonder if anyone considered using suspended platforms, which are so adaptable with multi-decks. Often with scaffold of this size and complexity a lot of its stands idle for much of the time just supporting more idle scaffolding above. In addition, as the decks of a surrounding platform are lowered, I doubt that the bell noise would be such a problem.

One of the last conservation projects that I have been involved with was The Rock Mill. A windmill that was built in 1826 to grind corn into flour for the area around Washington, West Sussex and converted into an attractive house in 1918-1920. At the time of the conversion the mill still had its patent sweeps with a beehive roof and a penthouse extension. It is believed the machinery, stones (French burrs) etc. had been sold to other mills.

The converted mill was lived in until 1962 and was later to become the offices of the sand pit adjoining the mill. Between then and when I went to the mill it had been badly vandalised with everything of value ripped out and windows broken allowing water to pour in – a very sad looking mill. We were asked to assist the architect to provide access for a survey and to make the building water tight.

We spent a few days going over the mill with ropes, bosun's chairs etc. with the architect getting a closer look at the slim but remarkably strong structure. Although it had been converted to a home the body of the mill was all original and when we removed some of the newer boarding to our and the architect's surprise the original cladding was still there. It was like reading a book on windmill history. I can only hope that our assistance helped and that this old mill is again restored for future generations.

As I get to the end of my views on the conservation and restoration of our historic buildings I wonder if I have done enough or sat on my soap box and shouted enough about the waste of our very limited resources. Although I have spent many years mainly working on churches I have been privileged to witness only a tiny part of the church maintenance and restoration program, but I have still seen such a waste of time and resources. Magnify this a few hundred fold and perhaps you start to see the true figure.

We all complain how the younger generation doesn't seem interested. Us oldies always complain that they are only interested in their phones, maybe true! But when I was young the oldies said that youngsters were only interested in driving and pulling, again true, generally! But, then and now, there are always enough keen youngsters who, if encouraged, would get very interested in the restoration and conservation of their heritage.

I spent a lot of time when working on churches in many beautiful villages and small towns speaking to youngsters. In most villages the school is built very near the church and the church is probably the best local history source available.

We usually find that when you are working on the local church the children will be doing a project prompted by our work. We were often asked to go into the school and give a short talk (usually a long talk with me) and although I have given many talks to adult associations, it is always the youngsters who ask the most intelligent questions. I certainly hope some of these youngsters go on to perhaps be steeplejacks, steeplejills or conservationists.